An Organic Chemistry Monograph
Consultant Editor: M. F. Grundon, The Queen's University, Belfast

ALICYCLIC CHEMISTRY

Oldbourne Chemistry Series

Alicyclic Chemistry

G. H. WHITHAM, B.Sc., Ph.D

Oxford University

An OLDBOURNE book

published by

MACDONALD TECHNICAL & SCIENTIFIC

London

MACDONALD & CO. (PUBLISHERS) LTD.

St. Giles House, 49\50 Poland Street, London, W.1.

© *Oldbourne Book Co. Ltd. 1963*

SBN 356 02226 9

2nd Impression 1965
3rd Impression 1968

Printed in Great Britain
by Spottiswoode, Ballantyne & Co. Ltd.
London and Colchester

PREFACE

Organic chemistry often suffers from subdivision into separate cells of specialization which may prevent an appreciation of the subject as an 'organic' whole. Nevertheless, the field of alicyclic chemistry is worthy of individual consideration for the many interesting illustrations it provides of the effect of variations in molecular architecture on the reactions of organic compounds. Traditionally it is in this field that the undergraduate is first encouraged to think chemically in three-dimensional terms and for that reason alicyclic chemistry can be a keystone in the training of the organic chemist.

In this book I have tried to encompass, in a relatively small space, the broad trends which I feel to be of especial significance. The approach throughout has been illustrative rather than exhaustive and the intention has been to try to establish the principles on which present-day thinking in alicyclic chemistry is based, starting at about the level of the second-year honours chemist.

Inevitably some of the hypotheses presented will not stand the test of time. In particular, I may be criticized for dwelling over long on the concept of 'non-classical' carbonium ions. However, I feel that all students of alicyclic chemistry should be acquainted with this theory which has so strongly influenced thinking about rearrangement reactions.

One word of advice, which cannot be too strongly emphasized: no real understanding of the structure and stereochemistry of alicyclic molecules is possible without frequent reference to molecular models. For small rings and some bridged rings the conventional ball and stick models are acceptable, but for an appreciation of the conformational aspects of six-membered rings Dreiding models (available in this country from L. Light and Co., Ltd.) are highly recommended.

Finally, I would like to thank my wife for typing the manuscript, Mr. A. J. Bellamy for reading through it, and Dr. Michael Grundon who, as editor of the series, gave valuable advice and counsel.

March, 1963   G. H. WHITHAM

CONTENTS

CHAPTER 1

INTRODUCTION—GENERAL PROPERTIES
OF ALICYCLIC SYSTEMS

Organic molecules containing rings formed by the junction of carbon atoms may be classified as carbocyclic compounds. Within this class two sub-divisions can be recognized, namely alicyclic and aromatic compounds. Alicyclic compounds comprise the majority of carbocyclic systems, both saturated and unsaturated, and are more akin to aliphatic compounds in their properties. In contrast, aromatic compounds possess special properties due to the presence of a closed π-electron system as in benzene.

Alicyclic compounds are of interest both for their own sake and because many natural products are representatives of this structural type. Thus the majority of terpenes and steroids and many alkaloids are built up primarily of alicyclic ring systems, some of them of considerable complexity. A more detailed knowledge of the chemistry of the simpler basic ring types will, therefore, provide a foundation for an understanding of the chemistry of natural products.

Historically, alicyclic chemistry has seen three broad phases. First, a preparative 'stamp collecting' phase in which many ring compounds were synthesized 'because they were there'. Secondly, a phase dominated by the so-called Baeyer strain theory (discussed below) in which some attempt was made to interpret the influence of ring size on syntheses and reactions. And thirdly, the most recent phase, in which the more refined ideas of stereochemistry and reaction mechanism have been developed, with the ultimate aim of providing a full understanding of the properties of alicyclic systems. Throughout all these phases cross-fertilization with ideas from natural product chemistry has provided a constant stimulus; many important concepts, first developed in the realm of natural products, were only later generalized by application to the more fundamental alicyclic systems.

Nomenclature. The basic building units of alicyclic compounds are the saturated monocyclic hydrocarbons whose names are derived by adding the prefix 'cyclo' to the name of the corresponding acyclic saturated unbranched hydrocarbon; e.g., cyclopropane (1) and cyclohexane (2). For convenience of representation such rings are often

1

written as in formulae (3) and (4) respectively. Here the apex of each angle represents a methylene group.

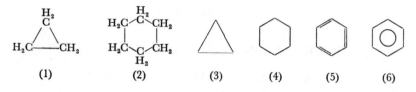

(1)   (2)   (3)   (4)   (5)   (6)

Care should be taken to distinguish clearly between a cyclohexane ring (4) and a benzene ring. The latter should be written either as a Kekulé form (5) or as in formula (6) with a circle to represent the 'aromatic sextet'.

Alicyclic compounds bearing functional groups are named according to the standard conventions and a few examples will illustrate the procedure: e.g., cyclopropanol (7), cyclobutanone (8), cyclopentene (9), methyl cyclohexyl ketone (10) and cyclohepta-2,6-dienone (11).

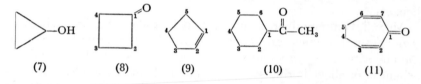

(7)   (8)   (9)   (10)   (11)

Difficulty is often experienced in the naming of bicyclic compounds. Except for a few cases where trivial names, e.g., decalin (decahydronaphthalene) (12), are used, the following rule is applied. 'Saturated alicyclic hydrocarbon systems consisting of two rings only, having two or more atoms in common, take the name of an open chain hydrocarbon containing the same total number of carbon atoms preceded by the prefix "bicyclo-". The number of carbon atoms in each of the three bridges connecting the two tertiary carbon atoms is introduced in brackets in descending order': e.g., bicyclo[1,1,0]butane (13), bicyclo[2,2,1]heptane (14) and bicyclo[3,2,1]octane (15). These planar formulae give a poor impression of the spatial arrangement of the atoms and it will usually be more instructive to employ three-dimensional representations for this type of molecule, e.g., bicyclo[2,2,1]heptane (16).

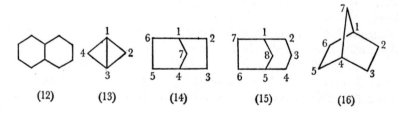

(12)   (13)   (14)   (15)   (16)

Stereochemistry. Substituted cycloalkanes can often exist as geometrical isomers. Thus, relative to the plane of the ring, substituents may be directed either above or below the plane. If two substituents are on the same side of the plane of the ring they are said to be *cis* to one another, if on opposite sides of the plane they are *trans*. A number of methods are in common usage for the two dimensional representation of geometrical isomerism in cyclic molecules. We shall employ the system whereby, with the plane of the ring in the plane of the paper, substituents above the plane are designated by thickened bonds and substituents below the plane by dotted bonds: e.g. *cis*-1,2-dimethylcyclopentane may be represented either by (17) or (18) and *trans*-1,4-dimethylcycloheptane by (19).

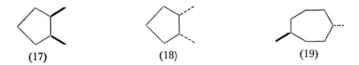

(17)   (18)   (19)

It should be noted that many alicyclic compounds are obtained as racemates which are capable of resolution into optically-active (enantiomeric) forms. Consider, for example, the two geometrical isomers of cyclopropane dicarboxylic acid. Each isomer contains two asymmetric carbon atoms and the *trans*-acid, which does not have a plane of symmetry, can exist as two separate optical enantiomers (20) and (21), one of which is dextro-rotatory and the other laevo-rotatory. The *cis*-isomer (22) possesses the plane of symmetry indicated by the broken line; it is therefore an internally-compensated or *meso*-form (cf. tartaric acid) and cannot be resolved into enantiomers.

In rings composed of an even number of carbon atoms the *trans*-disubstituted isomer with substituents at opposite corners of the ring, e.g., a *trans*-1,4-disubstituted cyclohexane, cannot sustain optical activity. This isomer has a mirror plane through the carbon atoms bearing the two substituents.

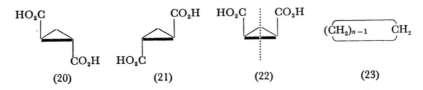

(20)   (21)   (22)   (23)

Classification of Alicyclic Compounds. Monocyclic hydrocarbons of general formula (23) can extend from the smallest ring, cyclopropane, (23, $n = 3$) to very large rings whose size is in theory limitless. In fact the largest ring known to date has $n = 54$. To simplify discussion, alicyclic compounds may be divided into four main groups (i) small rings where $n = 3$ and 4; (ii) normal rings, $n = 5$, 6 and 7; (iii) medium rings, $n = 8$–11 inclusive and (iv) large rings, n greater than 11. This classification is not entirely arbitrary since, as we shall see, there are certain properties which are characteristic of compounds within a given class.

Strain Theory. The internal angles of regular polygons possessing three, four, five and six members are respectively 60, 90, 108 and 120°. On the other hand the tetrahedral $C\!\!-\!\!\overset{\frown}{C}\!\!-\!\!C$ angle is 109° 28'. In considering these facts the German chemist A. von Baeyer was led, in 1885, to enunciate what is now known as the 'Baeyer Strain Theory'. He reasoned that the molecules of cyclopropane and cyclobutane are 'strained' because the $C\!\!-\!\!\overset{\frown}{C}\!\!-\!\!C$ bond angles are forced to be appreciably smaller than the preferred angle. In contrast the molecule of cyclopentane can be constructed with virtually no angle strain. In the original theory cyclohexane was also considered to be planar, which would require an expansion of the $C\!\!-\!\!\overset{\frown}{C}\!\!-\!\!C$ angle from the tetrahedral value. However, this aspect of the theory need not concern us further since, as we shall see later, cyclohexane is now known to be a puckered molecule free from angle strain.

When these ideas were proposed most of the known alicyclic compounds possessed five- and six-membered rings and only few examples of the smaller rings existed. This was used by Baeyer as circumstantial evidence for his contention that small rings are less stable than normal rings. Although many small ring compounds are now known, and this sort of evidence would not be acceptable today, there is good evidence, as we shall see, that small ring compounds are indeed less stable than their counterparts with normal rings. Baeyer's angle strain hypothesis still provides a useful qualitative explanation, although its physical basis has been considerably changed (see Chapter 3).

A quantitative comparison of the relative thermochemical stabilities* of the cycloalkanes may be derived from their heats of combustion. The enthalpy excess of a given cycloalkane $(CH_2)_n$ relative to a hypothetical ring of the same size constructed from cyclohexane CH_2 units is given by:

$$\text{Enthalpy excess} = -\left[\varDelta H_{(n)} - \frac{\varDelta H(C_6H_{12}) \cdot n}{6}\right]$$

where $\varDelta H_{(n)}$ is the heat of combustion of the cycloalkane $(CH_2)_n$, and $\varDelta H(C_6H_{12})$ is the heat of combustion of cyclohexane. In this way the

---

* The distinction between thermochemical stability, based on enthalpy differences $(\varDelta H)$, and thermodynamic stability, based on free energy differences $(\varDelta F)$ should be noted.

stability of a cycloalkane is expressed relative to that of cyclohexane. Values of this enthalpy excess for the first ten cycloalkanes are tabulated:

$n =$	3	4	5	6	7	8	9	10	11	12
enthalpy excess kcal./mole	27·6	26·0	6·5	0	6·3	9·6	12·6	12·0	11·0	3·6

Cyclohexane is thus the most stable of these cycloalkanes, and this reinforces the statement, already made, that it has a puckered strainless ring. Cycloheptane and cyclopentane are somewhat less stable than cyclohexane while cyclopropane and cyclobutane are relatively much less stable. This is good evidence for Baeyer type effects in these small ring molecules. In addition, medium sized ring hydrocarbons (n, 8–11) are also seen to be significantly less stable than those with normal rings. In this sense medium rings are often spoken of as being strained and to distinguish such strain from the Baeyer strain present in small rings it is sometimes called 'non-classical strain'. The origin of non-classical strain in medium rings will be considered in greater detail in Chapter 6; for the time being it may be stated that it is in part due to unfavourable interactions between non-bonded hydrogen atoms. In large rings, such interactions become less important and the enthalpy excess returns to a value compatible with a relatively strain free system.

RING SIZE EFFECTS

Although we shall be discussing the individual ring systems at length in the later chapters, it is convenient at this stage to consider a few of their properties to see how they are affected by a variation in ring size.

Reactions which are particularly prone to ring size effects are those in which a change in coordination number occurs at a ring carbon atom, e.g., a change from tetrahedral (sp^3 hybridization) to trigonal (sp^2 hybridization) or vice versa. As always, such reactions may be either (*a*) equilibrium controlled, when the outcome of the reaction depends only on the respective thermodynamic stabilities of the starting materials and products, or (*b*) kinetically controlled, when the important factor is the free energy difference between reactants and transition state. Only one typical example of each type will be quoted here to illustrate the operation of ring size effects, and no attempt will be made to provide a detailed explanation for the individual cases. This can be more appropriately left for the later chapters of the book.

5

(*a*) *Equilibrium Controlled Reactions.* One example of such a reaction is the addition of hydrogen cyanide to a cyclic ketone, i.e. cyanohydrin formation. The position of equilibrium is usually expressed in terms of the dissociation constant (K) of the cyanohydrin:

$$(\overbrace{CH_2)_{n-1}} \quad C{\stackrel{OH}{\diagdown}}_{CN} \underset{\longleftarrow}{\overset{K}{\longrightarrow}} (\overbrace{CH_2)_{n-1}} \quad C{=}O + HCN$$

Two main factors will influence the position of equilibrium for such a reaction in cyclic systems. Firstly, the preferred internal bond angle for the tetrahedral cyanohydrin is about 111° while that for the trigonal carbonyl group is approximately 120°. A ketone subject to angle strain (i.e. with a C—$\widehat{CO}$—C bond angle significantly less than 120°) will, therefore, undergo a release of strain on conversion to the cyanohydrin. The cyanohydrin of such a ketone is thus expected to have a relatively low dissociation constant. Secondly, if the cyano and hydroxyl groups in the cyanohydrin are subject to non-bonded interactions with other atoms in the remainder of the molecule, then dissociation of the cyanohydrin to the ketone will result in a relief of these interactions.

The experimentally determined dissociation constants of cyclic ketone cyanohydrins (see table) show a great variation with ring size, and clearly demonstrate the operation of ring size effects.

n	5	6	7	8	9	10	11	12	13	14
$K \times 10^2$	2·1	0·1	13	86	170	v. high	112	31	26	6

(*b*) *Kinetically Controlled Reactions.* For the prediction of the relative rates of a particular reaction in a series of cycloalkane derivatives, an assessment of the energy situation for the transition state of the reaction has to be made. Clearly such predictions will be less securely based than those concerning equilibrium reactions. Nevertheless the general trend seems fairly clear.

One example is the relative rates of acetolysis of a series of cycloalkyl tosylates (toluene-*p*-sulphonates), i.e., the relative rates of liberation of toluene-*p*-sulphonic acid on heating in acetic acid. In all probability the rate determining step of this reaction is an S_N1 heterolysis:

$$(\overbrace{CH_2)_{n-1}} \quad CH{-}OT_s \longrightarrow (\overbrace{CH_2)_{n-1}} \quad CH^{\oplus} + OT_s^{\ominus}$$

$$T_s = p{-}CH_3.C_6H_4.SO_2{-}$$

A ring carbon atom has thus changed from tetrahedral to essentially trigonal coordination on going from the starting state to the transition state. A cycloalkyl tosylate which is already subject to angle strain in the starting state will be forced to react by way of an even more strained transition state. It should, therefore, acetolyse relatively slowly. Conversely, release of strain will accompany the formation of the transition state from a tosylate which possesses internal strain in the ground state due to unfavourable non-bonded interactions. Such a cycloalkyl tosylate should acetolyse relatively rapidly.

First order rate constants for acetolysis of a series of cycloalkyl tosylates are tabulated below. Here again pronounced ring size effects are found and roughly the expected trends are observed. The main exception is cyclobutyl tosylate, and there is good reason for believing that special effects are operating in this case (see Chapter 3).

n	3	4	5	6	7	8	9	10	11	12	13
relative k at 70°	2×10^{-5}*	11·3	14·0	1·0	25·3	191	172	380	48·9	3·25	1·32

* Approximate value.

INFRARED CARBONYL STRETCHING BANDS OF CYCLIC KETONES

Another property which shows pronounced ring size effects is the position of the carbonyl stretching band in the infrared spectra of cyclic non-conjugated ketones. The frequency at which this absorption occurs is very sensitive to the C—$\overset{\frown}{CO}$—C bond angle. A normal straight chain ketone such as acetone with an angle of 116° absorbs at 1720 cm.$^{-1}$. In ketones with a smaller angle the carbonyl band occurs at higher frequencies while ketones with increased angles absorb at lower frequencies. Some values for normal cyclic ketones are tabulated and refer to solutions in carbon tetrachloride with the exception of cyclopropanone which was in the gas phase adsorbed on a solid matrix.

n	3	4	5	6	7	8	9	straight chain
$\nu_{max.}$ cm.$^{-1}$	1815	1788	1746	1715	1703	1703	1702	1720

The frequency of the carbonyl band is thus of considerable value in the determination of the ring size of cyclic ketones. It should, however, be emphasized that these typical values can be markedly affected by increased angle strain and that the determining factor is the bond angle, e.g. highly strained cyclopentanones may absorb in regions considered typical of cyclobutanones.

The carbonyl stretching frequencies of medium ring ketones indicate that the C—ĈO—C bond angles are significantly larger than the corresponding angle of cyclohexanone; this is in agreement with recent X-ray structure determinations on medium ring compounds (see Chapter 6).

Suggestions for Further Reading (Chapter I)

1. H. C. BROWN, 'Centenary Lecture', *J. Chem. Soc.*, 1956, 1248—a discussion of the effect of steric strain on the reactions of cyclic molecules and other compounds.
2. V. PRELOG, 'Centenary Lecture', *J. Chem. Soc.*, 1950, 420, provides a basis for some of the data used in this chapter.

CHAPTER 2

SYNTHESIS OF ALICYCLIC COMPOUNDS

Very many methods have been applied to the synthesis of alicyclic compounds and it is not proposed to deal with them exhaustively here. Instead a rough division of the reaction types under mechanistic headings will be attempted and a few examples of each will be discussed in order to illustrate the factors involved.

FORMATION OF ALICYCLIC COMPOUNDS FROM ACYCLIC PRECURSORS

The cyclization reactions of aliphatic compounds can be conveniently grouped under two headings: (1) those in which one carbon–carbon bond is formed at a time, and (2) those in which two carbon–carbon bonds are formed virtually simultaneously. The former group is more widely encountered but the second group contains a number of interesting reactions which often provide a simple route to otherwise inaccessible compounds.

(1) Formation of One Bond at a Time

Intramolecular Nucleophilic Displacements. These are simply extensions of nucleophilic displacement reactions to compounds in which the nucleophile and leaving group are part of the same molecule:

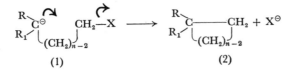

$$(1) \qquad\qquad (2)$$

For the formation of carbocyclic rings the nucleophilic centre must be a carbanion and thus either one or both of the groups R and R_1 should be capable of stabilizing the neighbouring negative charge. The leaving group $X^{\ominus}$ is usually a halide or tosylate ion.

A typical example of such a reaction is the following synthesis, due to Perkin, of cycloalkane carboxylic acids; an intramolecular malonate condensation occurs:

9

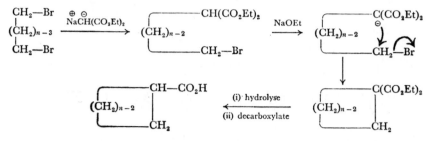

This reaction is applicable to the synthesis of rings of size $n = 3$ to $n = 6$ inclusive.

Since the ring closure step is irreversible, this type of synthesis is kinetically controlled, and is therefore most suitable for studying the influence of ring-size on the rate of reaction.

By transition state theory, the rate constant k_r of a reaction is given by the relation:

$$k_r = \frac{kT}{h} . e^{-\Delta F\ddagger/RT}$$

The free energy of activation ($\Delta F\ddagger$) is made up of an enthalpy term ($\Delta H\ddagger$) and an entropy term ($\Delta S\ddagger$), i.e. $\Delta F\ddagger = \Delta H\ddagger - T\Delta S\ddagger$, and it is thus to be expected that two factors will operate in irreversible ring closure reactions. Firstly, the enthalpy term should roughly parallel the thermochemical stability of the ring being formed (cf. p. 4). Hence the enthalpy of activation for the formation of small rings is expected to be larger than that for normal rings. However, considering the entropy term, which reflects the probability of reaching the transition state of the reaction, the more atoms whose motions have to be restricted in the process the more negative the entropy of activation. In other words, the larger the size of the ring being formed the more negative is $\Delta S\ddagger$. For the formation of small rings the two terms will work in opposite directions, since the larger enthalpies of activation tend to reduce the rate constant whereas the more positive entropies of activation (compared with larger rings) will tend to increase the rate constant. The relative importance of these two opposing effects is not easy to predict and is best discussed in relation to experimental observations.

Reliable rate studies on the formation of a series of carbocyclic rings have not been made, but values are available for the rates of ring closure of ω-aminoalkyl bromides (3) which are mechanistically analogous:

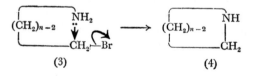

(3)   (4)

This particular system also has the advantage that it concentrates attention on the ring closure step whereas the related carbanion reaction $(1) \rightarrow (2)$ is complicated by the prior equilibrium step in which the carbanion is formed. The following relative rate constants for the reaction $(3) \rightarrow (4)$ are observed:

n	3	4	5	6	7	10	15
rel. k	0·12	0·002	100	1·7	0·028	10^{-8}	3×10^{-4}

A combination of the above two effects has thus given the five-membered ring pride of place over the other ring sizes. Although the six-membered ring is thermochemically more stable than the five-membered ring the transition state for its formation requires the restriction of more atomic motions, thereby resulting in a more negative entropy term which offsets the expected decrease in enthalpy of activation. For formation of the three-membered ring, although the motions of fewer atoms are being restricted, considerable angle strain in the transition state results in a high enthalpy of activation which overrides the entropy term. However, although the four-membered ring is thermochemically more stable than the three-membered ring, it is formed less readily due to the dominating effect of a more negative entropy of activation.

Also of interest in the above list of relative rate values is the very low rate of formation of the ten-membered ring, which is clearly due to the effect of non-classical strain on the enthalpy of activation.

The above factors affecting ring closure reactions have been considered in some detail since they can be expected to apply in all cases where kinetic control is operating. The reasonable rate of ring closure of the three-membered ring shows that such methods are quite suitable for the synthesis of cyclopropane derivatives. An interesting example which involves an S_N2' displacement on an allylic bromide is given by:

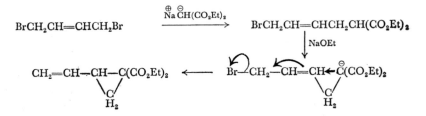

Intramolecular Carbonyl Addition Reactions. Many ketone and ester condensation reactions which have been used in aliphatic chemistry for the formation of new carbon to carbon bonds can be adapted to the synthesis of alicyclic rings by so choosing the substrate that intramolecular reaction can occur.

Such reactions are commonly carried out under basic conditions and involve addition of a resonance stabilized carbanion (e.g. enolate ion) to a suitable carbonyl function. The initial ring closure stage may be expressed in the following general form:

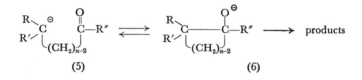

$$(5) \qquad\qquad (6)$$

Here the carbon bearing the negative charge should be flanked by one or more groupings capable of stabilizing the carbanion (cf. footnote on p. 13). R'' may be an alkyl, aryl or alkoxyl group, depending on the particular type of condensation reaction.

The subsequent steps depend on the constitution of the particular compound undergoing reaction, but one general feature of all reactions of this type may be recognized now. This is, that since the ring closure step and, almost invariably, the later steps are reversible it is necessary that the end product should be thermodynamically more stable than the starting material. It is not to be expected, therefore, that three- and four-membered rings can be synthesized in this way since they will clearly be destabilized with respect to starting material by angle strain. Non-classical strain also ensures that medium rings cannot be prepared by such methods. Intramolecular carbonyl addition reactions are thus pre-eminently of use for the synthesis of five- and six-membered ring compounds.

We may now turn to a consideration of some specific examples of this reaction type.

When R'' in formula (5) is an alkyl or aryl group and the carbanion activating group is a ketone or aldehyde function, we have the intramolecular condensation of a diketone or dialdehyde, e.g., the ethoxide ion induced cyclization of 4,4-dimethylheptane-2,6-dione (7).

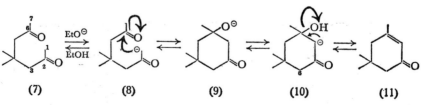

$$(7) \qquad (8) \qquad (9) \qquad (10) \qquad (11)$$

Ethoxide ion abstracts a proton from $C_{(1)}$ of (7) to give the carbanion*
(8) which then undergoes ring closure by nucleophilic addition to the
other carbonyl group. The resulting oxy-anion (9) undergoes proton
exchange with removal of the acidic proton α- to the carbonyl group to
form the new carbanion (10). The latter loses hydroxide ion (so-called
β-elimination process) to give the unsaturated ketone (11) which is the
product of the reaction. It may be pointed out that only those equilibria
which lead to the final product are shown in the above sequence. Other
equilibria do, of course, exist, e.g., those involving abstraction of a proton
from $C_{(3)}$ in (7) and from $C_{(6)}$ in (10), but are omitted for the sake of clarity
and brevity.

Utilizing the guiding principle that only five- and six-membered rings
can be obtained in such a reaction we can readily understand why 1,4-
and 1,6-diketones, cf. (12) and (13) respectively, afford five-membered
rings as shown, while 1,5- and 1,7-diketones (14) and (15) give six-
membered rings in such ketone condensations. The above case of the
diketone (7) provides a specific example of a 1,5-diketone condensation.

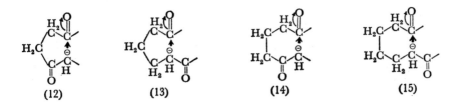

(12)   (13)   (14)   (15)

When the substrate is symmetrical, e.g., diketone (7), there is no
ambiguity about the product since the same compound is obtained
regardless of whether the ring closure occurs between $C_{(1)}$ and $C_{(6)}$ or $C_{(7)}$
and $C_{(2)}$. With unsymmetrical substrates a mixture of the two possible
products will in general result, provided that the attacking carbanion
carbon in both cases bears an additional hydrogen atom, i.e. so that a
final dehydration step such as (10)→(11) can occur. When only one of the
two possible modes of cyclization can lead to a subsequent dehydration
step then this particular path will be favoured. Clearly one product will
also be obtained when only one of the carbonyl groups in an unsymmetrical dicarbonyl compound is enolizable, e.g., cyclization of the

---

* It should be remembered that the carbanion (8) can be formed because it is stabilized by
delocalization of the negative charge on to oxygen, i.e. in resonance terminology the anion
may be expressed as:

$$\left[\overset{\ominus}{-}CH-\overset{\overset{\displaystyle O}{\|}}{C}- \quad \longleftrightarrow \quad -CH=\overset{\overset{\displaystyle O^{\ominus}}{}}{C}- \right]$$

1,6-ketoaldehyde (16) gives the unsaturated ketone (18) *via* the carbanion (17):

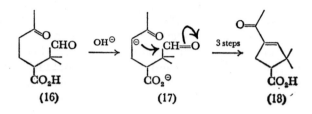

In certain circumstances a diketone cyclization may stop at the initial stage [corresponding to (6) in the general scheme]; one example of this will be encountered later (p. 17).

Diketone cyclization reactions can also be carried out under acid catalysed conditions, e.g., using hydrochloric acid in acetic acid. Under such circumstances enol rather than enolate ion intermediates are involved and relative rates of the various steps will be considerably altered. However, similar factors will govern the types of products formed.

Another group of reactions [(5)→(6); R″ = alkoxyl] involves the addition of a carbanion to an ester group. Such an intramolecular acylation reaction may be exemplified by the condensation of di-esters to β-keto-esters; the so-called Dieckmann reaction. For example, diethyl adipate (19) undergoes cyclization under the influence of sodium ethoxide:

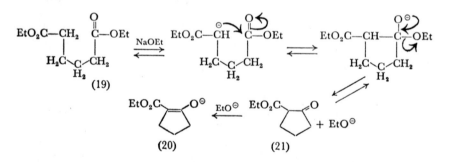

Carried out in this way the Dieckmann cyclization, as in the acetoacetic ester condensation itself, relies on the formation of the enolate ion of the β-keto-ester (20) to drive the reaction in the desired direction. Acidification of the reaction mixture then gives the free ketoester (21).

The corresponding reaction with diethylpimelate to give 2-carbethoxycyclohexanone works well, but in the case of diethyl suberate only traces of the seven-ring ketone are obtained, in agreement with the generalizations previously made. From the preparative point of view

Dieckmann cyclizations are probably most conveniently carried out using sodium hydride as the condensing agent. The first step, carbanion formation, is then effectively irreversible since gaseous hydrogen is evolved.

Another variant of the intramolecular acylation reaction involves a keto-ester instead of the di-ester employed in the Dieckmann reaction. Here a ketonic carbonyl group provides the activating influence for formation of the required carbanion, for example:

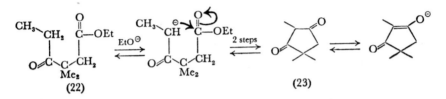

(22)   (23)

Again, as with the diketone condensation, the type and size of the ring produced is governed by the disposition of the ketonic carbonyl group with respect to the ester grouping. Thus, a 4-ketocarboxylic ester (22) and a 6-ketocarboxylic ester (24), give rise to five-membered ring β-diketones whereas a 5-ketocarboxylic ester (25), and a 7-ketocarboxylic ester (26), give six-membered ring β-diketones.

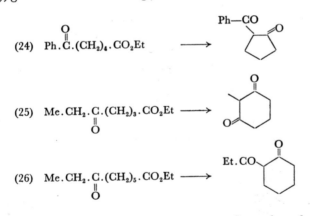

(24) $Ph.\overset{O}{\overset{\|}{C}}.(CH_2)_4.CO_2Et \longrightarrow$

(25) $Me.CH_2.\overset{}{\underset{\overset{\|}{O}}{C}}.(CH_2)_3.CO_2Et \longrightarrow$

(26) $Me.CH_2.\overset{}{\underset{\overset{\|}{O}}{C}}.(CH_2)_5.CO_2Et \longrightarrow$

Michael Reactions. The electrophilic character of a carbonyl group can be relayed by way of a conjugated double bond to the β-carbon atom, and the Michael reaction consists of the conjugate addition of a nucleophile to such an $\alpha\beta$-unsaturated carbonyl system:

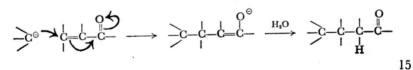

15

This type of carbon–carbon bond forming reaction is not often used for ring closure, although the following example may be cited:

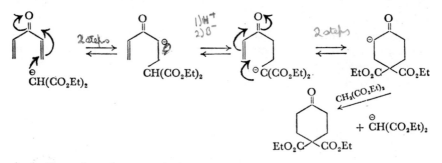

As indicated, only a catalytic amount of base is required to promote this reaction.

More usually, the Michael reaction has been employed for the synthesis of suitable precursors for those ring closure reactions which have already been discussed. Often conditions can be chosen so that the Michael reaction and the subsequent cyclization reaction occur consecutively without the isolation of any intermediates. Thus one can have Michael addition followed by an intramolecular nucleophilic displacement,

$$Cl.CH_2.CO_2Me \xrightarrow{\text{NaOMe}} Cl.CH.CO_2Me \longrightarrow$$

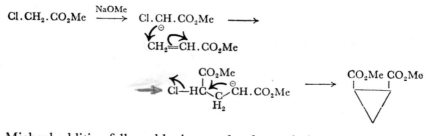

Michael addition followed by intramolecular acylation,*

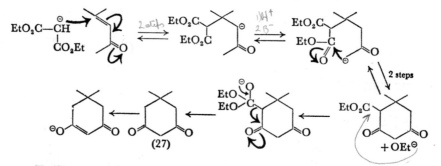

* In this sequence, the synthesis is of dimedone (27), the loss of an ethoxycarbonyl group occurs as indicated.

and Michael addition followed by a diketone condensation:

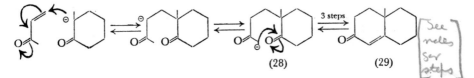

(28)   (29)

This latter reaction, due to Sir Robert Robinson, has been of considerable use in the synthesis of polycyclic natural products such as the steroids. Sometimes the reaction can be stopped at the initial carbonyl addition stage corresponding to formula (6) in the general scheme (p. 12). Thus intermediate ketols of the type (30) and (31) have been isolated from such reactions:

(30)   (31)

Under more vigorous basic (or acidic) conditions such ketols can be converted into the unsaturated ketones corresponding to (29).

Intramolecular Electrophilic Attack on a Benzene Ring or Double Bond. (a) Benzene Ring. This type of synthetic reaction is really just a straightforward intramolecular aromatic substitution. As an example we may take the internal Friedel–Craft synthesis using the acid chloride of 4-phenylbutyric acid.*

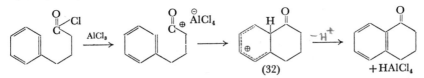

(32)   + HAlCl₄

The usual rules for orientation in aromatic substitution reactions apply in those cases where the benzene ring bears substituents, and the requirements of the transition state are such that six-membered rings are more readily formed than five-membered rings which, in turn, are more readily formed than seven-membered rings. Rings of other sizes cannot

* Formula (32) is equivalent to the resonance hybrid:

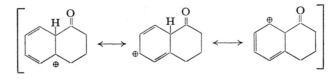

be satisfactorily prepared in this way. A convenient method of intra-molecular acylation involves treatment of the free acid with anhydrous hydrogen fluoride. This, and some of the earlier points, may be exempli-fied by the following reactions:

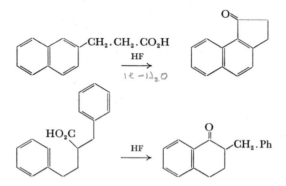

(b) _Double Bond._ Cyclization occurs when a carbonium ion is generated in a molecule that also possesses a double bond, one terminus of which is six atoms away from the cationic carbon atom. Such reactions are par-ticularly common among the terpenes and the illustrations used are taken from this field:

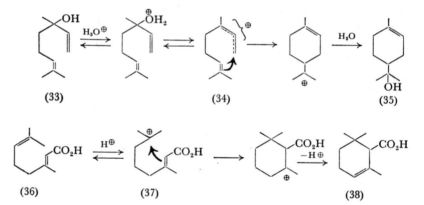

In the acid catalysed cyclization of linalool (33) to α-terpineol (35) the cationic centre is an allylic carbonium ion (34)* derived by protonation

* Using this symbolism the allyl carbonium ion would be represented by:

$$\overset{\oplus}{CH_2 \!=\!\!=\! CH \!=\!\!=\! CH_2}$$

This is equivalent to

$$\left[CH_2 \!=\! CH \!-\! \overset{\oplus}{CH_2} \quad \longleftrightarrow \quad \overset{\oplus}{CH_2} \!-\! CH \!=\! CH_2 \right]$$

18

of the allylic alcohol. For the cyclization of geranic acid (36) to α-cyclo-geranic acid (38) the required carbonium ion, cf. (37), is derived by Markownikow addition of a proton to the non-conjugated double bond. Acid catalysed cyclizations of this type lead almost invariably to cyclo-hexane derivatives. This seems to be due to the fact that a concerted anti-parallel addition can proceed directly to give the cyclohexane ring in the preferred chair conformation (see p. 52), for example:

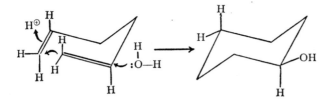

Cyclizations of this type have assumed considerable importance in connection with theories on the biogenesis of polycyclic natural products.

The Acyloin Condensation. An important cyclization reaction which is mechanistically different from any of those already considered is the so-called acyloin condensation of ω-dicarboxylic esters, e.g. (39). Under the influence of sodium in ether such esters undergo a reductive cycliza-tion forming, after work up of the reaction mixture, an acyloin (43). The following mechanism has been assigned:

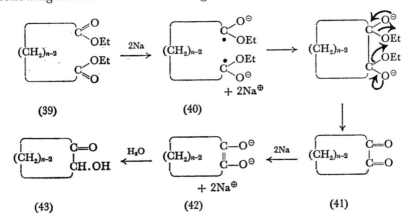

Two reductive stages occur, namely $(39) \rightarrow (40)$ and $(41) \rightarrow (42)$. Clearly, intermolecular reactions of the same type leading to dimeric, trimeric and higher acyloins would be expected to compete with the intramolecular reaction. However, these complications are minimized by carrying out the reaction at high dilution. An important feature of the acyloin condensation is that it is irreversible and so can be used for the

19

formation of medium and large ring acyloins. Even ten-membered rings possessing a maximum of non-classical strain can be synthesized in quite good yield, and it has been suggested that the polar ester groupings are brought together on the surface of the metal thereby overcoming the low probability factor (i.e. strongly negative entropy of activation) associated with the formation of large rings.

A modified technique, using sodium in liquid ammonia as the reducing agent, has been applied to formation of the corresponding normal ring acyloins.

(2) Formation of Two Bonds at a Time

The Diels-Alder Reaction. The Diels-Alder reaction, or diene synthesis, discovered by the German chemists Diels and Alder, consists of the addition of a conjugated diene to an activated double bond with formation of a six-membered ring. It has been widely employed for the synthesis of substituted cyclohexanes since its stereochemical consequences are often predictable. For reaction to take place it is necessary that the diene should be capable of existing in a *cisoid*-conformation,* e.g., butadiene (44); the 'activation' applied to the double bond is usually in the form of electron attracting groups symbolized by X in formula (45). The general reaction may thus be expressed as:

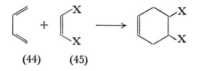

(44)   (45)

A typical *dienophile*, as a compound of general structure (45) is often called, is maleic anhydride (46) and the reaction between it and a diene is often used as a diagnostic test for a conjugated diene which can exist in a *cisoid*-conformation, e.g.:

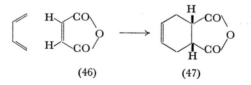

(46)   (47)

---

* The terms *cisoid* and *transoid* are used to denote the two extreme forms of the rotational 'isomers' about the single bond between the double bonds. Thus the *transoid*, preferred, conformation for butadiene is:

The product (47), tetrahydrophthalic anhydride, has the *cis*-stereo-chemistry shown. In general the geometry of the starting dienophile is preserved in the product of a Diels-Alder reaction. The most reactive dienophile known is tetracyanoethylene.

Reactive dienes such as cyclopentadiene (48) ,where the double bonds are fixed in a *cisoid* relationship, will react with relatively unreactive dienophiles, e.g., with vinyl acetate to give norbornenyl acetate (49), or with acetylene to give norbornadiene (50). This type of reaction is the main synthetic route to the norbornane (bicyclo[2,2,1]heptane) system.

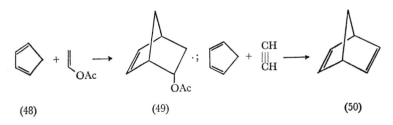

(48)   (49)   (50)

In the case of reaction of cyclopentadiene with, e.g. maleic anhydride, two possible modes of addition are, in principle, available. These are shown in (51) and (53) leading respectively to an *exo*-adduct* (52) or an *endo*-adduct* (54).

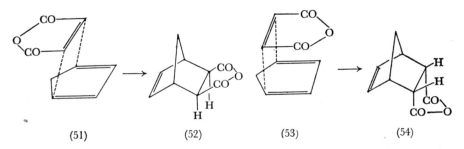

(51)   (52)   (53)   (54)

In practice it is found that the *endo*-adduct is often the kinetically controlled product of the reaction. This has led to the rule of maximum overlap of unsaturation in the transition state for predicting the stereo-chemical outcome of the Diels-Alder reaction. Thus in (53) the π-electrons of the anhydride carbonyl groups can overlap with the π-electron system of the diene; this is not possible in (51).

The mechanism of the Diels-Alder reaction, which clearly involves electronic reorganization in an activated complex, is a matter of con-siderable interest. However, due to the many factors involved it is a rather controversial issue and not properly discussed here.

* For definition of the terms *exo*- and *endo*- see p. 84.

Addition of One Double Bond to Another. Certain olefinic compounds containing 'activated' double bonds undergo cyclo-addition reactions with formation of cyclobutane rings. These reactions fall into two classes, firstly those in which two 'activated' olefins add together, (for example dimerization), and secondly those in which an 'activated' olefin adds to an 'unactivated' olefin. Ketenes are typical 'activated' olefins, and olefins that are heavily substituted with electron-attracting groups, for example fluoro-olefins also come into this category.

The thermal dimerization of tetrafluoroethylene (55) to octafluoro-cyclobutane (56) and 1,1-dichloro-2,2-difluoroethylene (57) to the halogenocyclobutane (58) provide instances of the reaction of activated olefins. Disubstituted ketenes such as dimethyl ketene (59) undergo an analogous dimerization to form 1,4-cyclobutanediones.

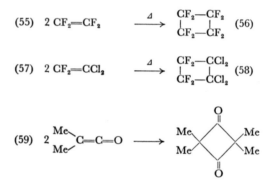

$$(55) \quad 2\ CF_2{=}CF_2 \quad \xrightarrow{\varDelta} \quad \begin{matrix} CF_2{-}CF_2 \\ | \quad\quad | \\ CF_2{-}CF_2 \end{matrix} \quad (56)$$

$$(57) \quad 2\ CF_2{=}CCl_2 \quad \xrightarrow{\varDelta} \quad \begin{matrix} CF_2{-}CCl_2 \\ | \quad\quad | \\ CF_2{-}CCl_2 \end{matrix} \quad (58)$$

Monosubstituted ketenes and ketene itself usually dimerize by addition of the double bond of one unit across the carbonyl group of the other, giving a β-lactone structure, e.g., diketene (60). However, cyclobutane derivatives are sometimes formed, thus methyl ketene (61) gives two dimers, one liquid which has the β-lactone structure and one solid, which has acidic properties, and is the enolic β-diketone (62).

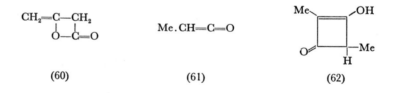

(60)   (61)   (62)

Examples of the addition of 'activated' to 'unactivated' double bonds include the addition of tetrafluoroethylene to ethylene to give the tetrafluorocyclobutane (63) and the addition of ketene to cyclopentadiene to form the bicyclic ketone (64).

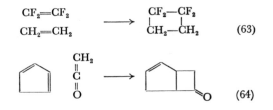

The latter reaction is particularly interesting since cyclo-addition giving the cyclobutane structure has occurred in preference to the alternative possibility of Diels-Alder type addition.

Compounds containing olefinic double bonds that are conjugated to a π-electron system will absorb ultra-violet light and can be 'activated' by irradiation with light of a suitable wavelength. Under these circumstances cyclobutane derivatives can often be produced for example, the truxillic acids (stereoisomers of 65) and the truxinic acids (stereoisomers of 66) are obtained by irradiation of cinnamic acid.

Addition of Carbenes to Double Bonds. Just as the addition of one double bond to another can result in cyclobutane ring formation so the addition of a divalent carbon intermediate—a *carbene**—affords a route to cyclopropane rings:

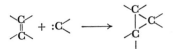

Such carbenes have only been recognized relatively recently as reactive intermediates in organic chemistry. They may be produced in a variety of ways, for example by treatment of chloroform with strong alkali. In this reaction the intermediate trichloromethyl anion (67), loses chloride ion to give dichlorocarbene (68) whose presence can be

---

* Carbenes are highly reactive species of transitory existence which possess an electron deficient carbon atom containing only six electrons in the outer shell. In addition they are divalent with two electrons not involved in chemical bonding. By Hund's rule each of these 'extra' electrons is probably located in a different orbital and thus carbenes have di-radical character.

demonstrated by reaction with an olefin such as cyclohexene to produce a dichlorocyclopropane:

(67)　　　　(68)

Carbenes may also be generated photochemically or pyrolytically from diazo compounds. For example, irradiation of diazomethane gives the parent carbene, methylene, and irradiation of diazoacetic ester gives carbethoxy-carbene.

$$CH_2 \overset{\oplus}{=} N \overset{\ominus}{=} N \quad \overset{h\nu}{\longrightarrow} \quad CH_2: + N_2$$

$$EtO_2C.CH \overset{\oplus}{=} N \overset{\ominus}{=} N \quad \overset{h\nu}{\longrightarrow} \quad EtO_2C.CH: + N_2$$

These photochemically or thermally produced carbenes are too reactive to add selectively to double bonds, and accompanying products result from attack on C–H bonds. Thus the reaction of photolytically generated methylene with propylene gives but-1-ene as well as methyl-cyclopropane:

$$CH_3{-}CH{=}CH_2 + CH_2: \quad \longrightarrow \quad CH_3{-}CH\underset{\underset{H_2}{C}}{\overline{\quad\quad}}CH_2 + CH_3{-}CH_2{-}CH{=}CH$$

The reactivity of such carbenes can be modified if they are generated in the presence of copper; apparently a copper-complexed carbene then results which is of lower reactivity and only cyclopropanes are obtained on reaction with olefins.

A general synthesis of cyclopropanes which may also involve a metal complexed carbene is the reaction of methylene di-iodide and zinc-copper couple on an olefin, for example:

FORMATION OF ALICYCLIC COMPOUNDS FROM
CYCLIC PRECURSORS

The methods of synthesis of alicyclic compounds starting from cyclic precursors come under two main headings: firstly, the various methods of reduction of benzenoid rings, which of course can only be used for cyclohexane rings, and secondly, ring expansion and ring contraction procedures which often allow the synthesis of relatively inaccessible ring compounds from more easily available starting materials.

(1) Reduction of Aromatic Compounds

(*a*) *Catalytic Hydrogenation.* One of the most useful procedures for the synthesis of substituted cyclohexane derivatives consists of the catalytic hydrogenation of appropriate aromatic precursors. Such hydrogenations are usually carried out under pressure using Raney nickel as the catalyst, e.g., the hydrogenation of *p*-t-butylphenol to a mixture of *cis*- (69) and *trans*-4-t-butylcyclohexanol (70).

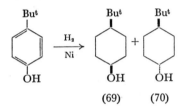

(69)   (70)

Catalytic hydrogenations, using Raney nickel as catalyst, tend to give mixtures of products where stereoisomerism is possible as in the above example. Platinum may also be used as catalyst under acidic conditions and the tendency then is for *cis*-addition to occur, i.e., all the hydrogen atoms introduced during the hydrogenation are on the same side of the ring.

(*b*) *Metal-Ammonia and Metal-Amine Reductions.* More interesting theoretically, and especially useful for the synthesis of unsaturated cyclohexane derivatives, are reductions of aromatic compounds using solutions of alkali metals in either ammonia (explored by A. J. Birch) or ethylamine (due to R. A. Benkeser). These reductions can be extremely complex and the precise outcome is strongly dependent on the particular substrate and reaction conditions. A full discussion would be outside the scope of this book and we can do no more than point out a few salient features.

On reduction of aromatic compounds with sodium or lithium in liquid ammonia in the presence of ethanol the usual course of the reaction is to give a 1,4-dihydrobenzene. Thus benzene yields 1,4-dihydrobenzene (71) itself.

$$\text{benzene} \xrightarrow[\text{liq. NH}_3,\ \text{EtOH}]{2\ \text{Na}} (71) + 2\text{Na}^{\oplus}$$

(71)

25

The precise mechanism of the reaction is still in some doubt but it probably involves consecutive one-electron additions to the aromatic ring:

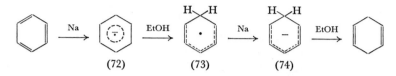

The anion-radical (72), formed on addition of one electron from sodium to the benzene ring, may be regarded as a resonance hybrid of canonicals of the type (75), (76) etc. Further reaction can usually occur only in the presence of a stronger 'acid' than ammonia such as ethanol, which can donate a proton to the anion radical to give the resonance stabilized radical (73), [i.e., (77), (78) etc.]. Addition of a further electron from sodium gives the anion (74), [i.e., (79), (80) etc.], which finally abstracts a proton from solvent to give 1,4-dihydrobenzene. Seemingly (80) is the most important contributor to the resonance hybrid.

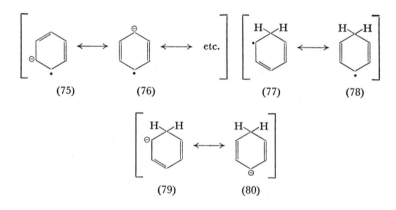

Where substituents, such as alkyl or alkoxyl groups are present on the aromatic ring, the dihydrobenzene formed is that with the maximum number of alkyl and alkoxyl groups attached to double bonds; e.g., anisole (81) gives the dihydroanisole (82) and the methyl ether of tetra-hydro-β-naphthol (83) gives the compound (84) on reduction.

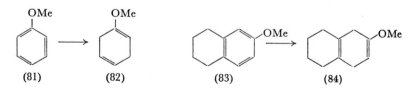

Conversely a carboxyl substituent, which can stabilize a negative charge on the α-carbon atom, yields a 1,4-dihydrobenzene with a carboxyl group attached to one of the saturated carbon atoms. Benzoic acid, for example, gives dihydrobenzoic acid (85)

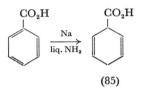

(85)

The vinyl ethers, e.g., (82) and (84), which result from the reduction of aromatic ethers, are especially useful since they can be converted into ketones on acidic hydrolysis. By suitable choice of conditions this can often be carried out in a stepwise fashion so as to give first the $\beta\gamma$-unsaturated ketone, e.g. (86), which, on more vigorous acid treatment, yields the $\alpha\beta$-unsaturated ketone, e.g. (87).

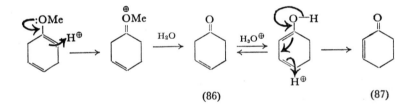

(86)   (87)

(2) Ring Expansion and Ring Contraction Procedures

Most of the common ring expansion procedures involve the generation of what is effectively an exocyclic primary carbonium ion adjacent to a ring carbon atom. Migration of a ring carbon–carbon bond then results in ring expansion, the driving force for the reaction being the rearrangement of a primary carbonium ion into a secondary or tertiary one:

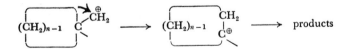

The new carbonium ion produced may then be stabilized by loss of a proton or by attack of solvent.

An example of this class of reaction is the Demjanow ring expansion in which the electron deficient exocyclic carbon atom is generated by deamination of a suitable primary amine with nitrous acid:

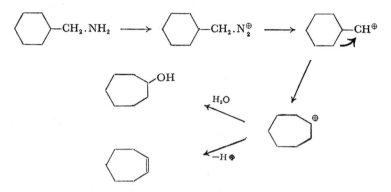

A modification of the above reaction which entails the deamination of a 1-hydroxycycloalkylmethylamine, e.g., (88) is more useful synthetically since only one product, the ring expanded ketone, is obtained.

DEMJANOV
TIFFENEAU

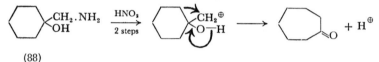

(88)

An alternative way of inducing the same sort of reaction involves addition of diazomethane to a cycloalkanone. Here, however, complications can occur since the intermediate, e.g., (89), can also lead to some exocyclic epoxide (91) as well as to the main reaction product, the ring expanded ketone (90). Additional impurities also arise by further interaction of the ring expanded ketone with diazomethane.

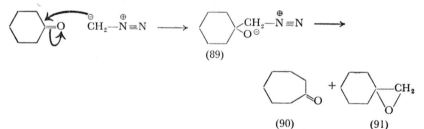

(89)

(90)   (91)

An interesting ring contraction procedure, which can be applied to the synthesis of small rings, is the Favorskii reaction of cyclic α-haloketones. This reaction proceeds, at least in certain cases, by way of an intermediate cyclopropanone such as (92) formed by intramolecular displacement of halide ion by the enolate ion of the ketone. The ready ring opening of the cyclopropanone by further attack of base is an expected consequence of angle strain in the three-membered ring.

28

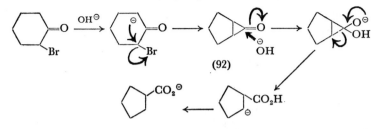

(92)

In a similar way α-bromocyclobutanone can be transformed into cyclopropane carboxylic acid on treatment with alkali. Presumably the highly strained bicyclo[1,1,0]ketone (93) is involved as an intermediate:

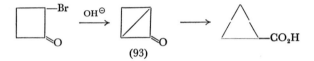

(93)

Another ring contraction procedure which also leads to cycloalkane carboxylic acids involves the ultraviolet irradiation of a cyclic α-diazo-ketone, e.g., α-diazocyclohexanone (94). Recalling that irradiation of diazomethane gives carbene the expected immediate product from irradiation of (94) is the keto-carbene (95). The latter rearranges to the ketene (96) which reacts with the nucleophilic solvent, water, to give the ring contracted acid (97).

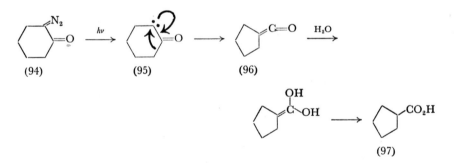

(94)   (95)   (96)

(97)

This reaction has been utilized in the synthesis of the highly strained bicyclo[2,1,1]hexane skeleton:

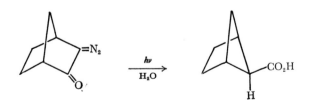

29

Suggestions for Further Reading (Chapter 2)

Details, both theoretical and experimental, of many of the reactions described in this chapter are to be found in the volumes of *Organic Reactions*, John Wiley and Sons, Inc., New York, N.Y. Particularly relevant chapters include:

'Formation of Cyclic Ketones by Intramolecular Acylation', W. S. JOHNSON, in Vol. 2.

'Diels–Alder Reaction', M. C. KLOETZEL, in Vol. 4.

'Acylation of Ketones to form β-Diketones', C. R. HAUSER, F. W. SWAMER and J. T. ADAMS, in Vol. 8.

'The Michael Reaction', E. D. BERGMANN, D. GINSBURG and R. PAPPO, in Vol. 10.

'Cyclo-addition Reactions', J. D. ROBERTS and C. M. SHARTS, in Vol. 12.

Chapter 3

SMALL RING COMPOUNDS

Cyclopropane, cyclobutane and their derivatives are of considerable interest to organic chemists since their special structures can lead to unusual properties and reactions. They provide, therefore, a critical testing ground for structural and mechanistic theories, and a straight-forward extrapolation of ideas forged in the field of aliphatic compounds often cannot be made. In addition, certain specially constituted deriva-tives of small ring compounds, some of which we shall be encountering later in this chapter, have achieved prominence in connection with theories of 'aromaticity'.

Structures of Cyclopropane and Cyclobutane. Chemically speak-ing cyclopropane occupies a position somewhere between ethylene on the one hand and cyclobutane on the other. The gradation of properties along the series; ethylene, cyclopropane, cyclobutane and cyclopentane is such that ethylene might be considered as the smallest ring, $(CH_2)_n$ where $n = 2$.

Ethylene, it will be remembered, may be considered to be built up of two sp^2 hybridized carbon atoms joined together, and to each of the hydrogen atoms, by a σ-bond, with the remaining two electrons of the double bond forming a π-bond (comprising two overlapping p-orbitals) at right angles to the plane of the molecule (1). This leads to an H—C—H bond angle of about 120°. The C—H bonds, which are made up from carbon sp^2 hybrid orbitals, thus have greater s-character than the C—H bonds of, e.g., methane, in which the carbon is sp^3 hybridized. Increase in the s-character of a bond results in a diminished bond length; thus the C—H bonds of ethylene are expected to be shorter than the C—H bonds of methane. In fact the C—H bond length for ethylene is 1·071 Å while that for methane is 1·094 Å. The shorter a bond is, the greater is its force constant and hence the higher the frequency of the stretching vibration. Thus C—H bonds attached to double bonds have C—H stretching bands in the infrared at higher frequencies than C—H bonds on saturated carbon atoms. Typically, olefinic C—H stretching bands occur in the region 3010–3090 cm.$^{-1}$ while C—H stretching bands for saturated alkanes are in the range 2850–2960 cm.$^{-1}$.

We are now in a position to consider the structure of cyclopropane and to compare it with ethylene. Infrared and Raman spectra indicate, in

31

agreement with the classical structure, that the carbon atoms of the three-membered ring are at the corners of an equilateral triangle and that the H—C—H plane is at right angles to the plane of the ring and bisects the C—$\widehat{C}$—C angle. Electron diffraction measurements have given the following bond lengths and angles: C—H, 1·08 Å; C—C, 1·54 Å; H—$\widehat{C}$—H, 118·2°; H—$\widehat{C}$—C, 116·4°. Of particular interest is the H—$\widehat{C}$—H angle which is close to that for an sp^2 hybridized atom. Also the C—H bond length is closer to that of ethylene than that of methane. In agreement with this the C—H stretching bands of cyclopropane occur in the infrared at 3000 and 3062 cm.⁻¹. These data uphold the statement that cyclopropane is intermediate in character between ethylene and a normal cycloalkane.

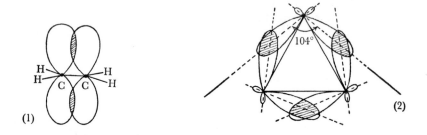

(1) (2)

In one molecular orbital representation for cyclopropane, the carbon atoms are considered to be so hybridized that the orbitals forming the ring bonds have greater p-character than those forming a normal sp^3 hybrid σ-bond. Thus the angle between these orbitals is somewhere between the tetrahedral angle (109° 28′) for sp^3-carbon orbitals and the angle for 'pure' p-orbitals (90°). The best compromise is at about 104° between the orbitals (2). Greater p-character of the orbitals forming the ring bonds must be balanced by increased s-character of the orbitals forming the C—H bonds as in ethylene. This accommodates satisfactorily the H—$\widehat{C}$—H bond angle and C—H bond length in cyclopropane. The electrons of the C—C linkages are thus localized in bent or 'banana'-like bonds and, due to the greater p-character of the constituent orbitals they are more polarizable than the electrons of normal σ-bonds. This representation of cyclopropane provides a rationalization for some of the similarities between a cyclopropane ring and a double bond which have been mentioned already. Further chemical similarities will be encountered in the ensuing discussion.

In the above model (2) for cyclopropane, the orbitals forming a C—C bond overlap less than in a normal σ-bond where the orbitals are directed along the line joining the two atoms. Most of the extra 'strain energy' of cyclopropane can be explained in terms of this less efficient overlap. We shall, however, continue to use the convenient term angle strain in this context.

The molecular structure of cyclobutane has also been determined by electron diffraction and the following dimensions found: c—c, 1·56 Å; c—h, 1·09 Å; h—$\widehat{c}$—h, 114°. Apparently the ring has a certain degree of flexibility and is, on average, non-planar. It appears that cyclobutane does not differ greatly from a 'classical' structure with bent bonds composed of sp^3 hybrid orbitals. Thus the extremes of properties shown by cyclopropane and its derivatives are not nearly so marked in cyclobutyl compounds. In this respect it is perhaps surprising that the thermochemical instability of cyclobutane with respect to cyclohexane (p. 5) is as much as it is. Although this can be partially accounted for by angle strain considerations it is likely that a significant contribution comes from a repulsion between the pairs of non-bonded carbon atoms which are only 2·27 Å apart. This repulsion probably also accounts for the somewhat longer c—c bonds in cyclobutane than in cyclopropane.

REACTIONS OF SMALL RING COMPOUNDS

We have seen that small ring compounds are thermochemically less stable than compounds with normal rings, and strain considerations of one sort or another can account for this instability. If we apply these ideas to the reactivity of ring systems we might expect small ring compounds to undergo ring opening reactions more readily than normal rings. Although, as will be seen, a rough parallelism of this sort is in fact found, it must be remembered that the rate of a kinetically controlled reaction depends on the free energy of activation and not on the relative thermodynamic stabilities of starting materials and products. Thus a simple relation between the ease of ring opening and the thermodynamic stability of small rings is only to be expected in so far as the higher energy of a strained ring results in a lower free energy of activation for the ring opening reaction. In other words, release of strain must have already occurred in the transition state.

Hydrogenation of cycloalkanes appears to satisfy these requirements. Thus, using hydrogen in the presence of a nickel catalyst, cyclopropane can be hydrogenolysed to n-propane at 80°, cyclobutane requires a temperature of 180° for conversion to n-butane, while cyclopentane is only cleaved to n-pentane at 300°. The relative ease of hydrogenolysis of cycloalkanes is thus qualitatively proportional to the degree of strain in the ring.

The ease of reaction of cyclopropane with electrophilic reagents such as halogens, halogen hydracids, sulphuric acid, aluminium chloride, etc., may be attributed to ring strain. However, an additional factor is that the more polarizable C—C bonds (increased *p*-character) of cyclopropane result in the formation of a low energy transition complex. Thus, not only are the thermodynamic requirements for reaction satisfied but also a reasonable route is available.

Cyclobutane, on the other hand, does not readily react with electrophilic reagents even though it is known to be appreciably strained in the thermochemical sense. In this case there is no reasonable mechanism for electrophilic attack by way of a transition state of low enough energy. However, if an activating group, i.e., in general terms an electron rich centre, is introduced on, or adjacent to, a cyclobutane ring, then such reactions do, in fact, occur readily. In this case a reasonable mechanism for ring opening is provided.

Reactions of Cyclopropanes with Electrophilic Reagents. It has already been mentioned that cyclopropane reacts readily with electrophilic reagents and we may now consider some specific examples of such reactions.

A simple case is the addition of bromine to cyclopropane to give 1,3-dibromopropane:

$$H_2C\text{----}CH_2 \diagdown \diagup CH_2 \quad \xrightarrow{Br_2} \quad Br.CH_2.CH_2.CH_2.Br$$

It may be compared with the reaction of bromine with ethylene to give 1,2-dibromoethane. In the latter case *trans*-addition occurs, probably by attack of bromide ion on an intermediate bromonium ion (3) (see p. 72).

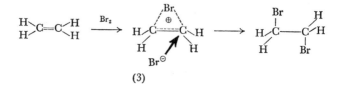

(3)

The bromonium ion (3) may be regarded for most purposes as a resonance hybrid of the four canonicals (4)–(7).

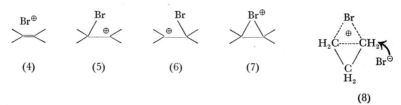

(4)   (5)   (6)   (7)   (8)

In the case of attack of bromine on a cyclopropane ring less is known about the mode of reaction but, by analogy with the double bond, it is possible that an intermediate ion such as (8) is involved.

Substitution of electron releasing groups (e.g., alkyl groups) on the cyclopropane ring facilitates the addition of bromine as expected for an electrophilic reaction and as found for substituted olefins. Thus methylcyclopropane (9) reacts more rapidly than cyclopropane itself with bromine to give 1,3-dibromobutane (10). Conversely the substitution of electron attracting groups in cyclopropane results in a diminished reactivity toward electrophilic attack, e.g., bromine reacts much less readily with the diester (11) than with cyclopropane. The effect of substituents on the relative ease of ring opening of cyclopropanes shows that strain is by no means the only consideration in the reactivity of small ring compounds.

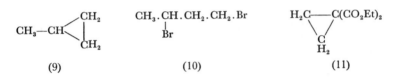

(9)   (10)   (11)

Addition of halogen hydracids to unsymmetrically substituted cyclopropanes leads to the interesting question as to which will be the preferred direction of ring opening. In fact, as with substituted olefins, addition occurs in a 'Markownikow' fashion, i.e. on addition of hydrogen bromide the hydrogen atom becomes attached to the *least* alkylated carbon atom and the bromine atom to the *most* alkylated carbon atom. Thus methylcyclopropane gives rise to 2-bromobutane:

$$CH_3-CH{\overset{CH_2}{\underset{CH_2}{\big<}}} \xrightarrow{HBr} CH_3.CH(Br).CH_2.CH_3$$

It is possible that an initial complex between the cyclopropane and a proton, e.g., (12) is formed which then undergoes isomerization to the most stable carbonium ion (13) (i.e. that with the most alkyl groups attached to the positively charged carbon atom), followed by addition of bromide ion:

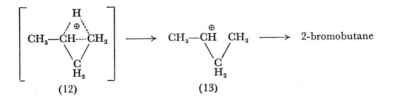

(12)   (13)

Another case is that of 1,1,2-trimethylcyclopropane which reacts with hydrogen bromide in an analogous fashion:

Ring cleavage with hydrogen bromide is sometimes used in the elucidation of the structure of natural products containing cyclopropane rings. Additional information is provided if deuterium bromide is used instead of hydrogen bromide since, if the position of the deuterium atom which is introduced can be determined, the other terminus of the original ring is indicated.

Although oxidation is fundamentally an electrophilic process, cyclopropanes, unlike olefins, are not oxidized readily. Clearly relief of ring strain does not occur in the transition state for oxidation of a small ring compound. The resistance of cyclopropanes to oxidation has frequently been of use in natural product chemistry: e.g., the terpene hydrocarbon carene (14) undergoes stepwise oxidation, firstly of the double bond, and then of the side chain, giving caronic acid (15). Further oxidation of caronic acid to dimethylmalonic acid does however occur to a limited extent.

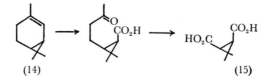

(14)   (15)

Reactions involving Change in Coordination at a Ring Carbon.

We have already briefly considered, in Chapter 1, the way in which 'angle strain' in small ring compounds can affect the course of reactions which involve a coordination change at a ring carbon atom. A few examples will now be discussed in greater detail.

For equilibrium processes, it will be remembered, a tetrahedral ring carbon atom is preferred over a trigonal one in small rings. Striking confirmation for this comes from cyclopropanone (16) which can only be fleetingly prepared in the gas phase and reacts with traces of moisture to form the stable hydrate (17).

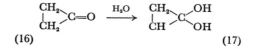

(16)   (17)

Similarly, cyclobutanones react readily with hydrogen cyanide to form cyanohydrins in high yield. Thus it appears that, as anticipated, the equilibrium is well on the side of the tetrahedrally coordinated cyanohydrin.

A related point concerns the difficulty of forming a carbanion on a cyclopropane ring. In the normal way the enolate ion of a ketone possessing a C—H bond α to the carbonyl group can be readily obtained by treatment with a suitable strong base. The resulting carbanion is stabilized by overlap with the π-electron system of the carbonyl group, i.e. it can exist as a resonance hybrid (18)↔(19). For maximum overlap to occur, however, the carbon atom α to carbonyl should be sp^2 hybridized thus putting the negative charge in a p-orbital, i.e. this carbon atom should be trigonal [cf. (20)]. Such an enolate ion will, therefore, be difficult to obtain if the carbanion carbon is a member of a three-membered ring.

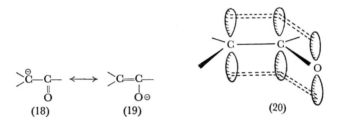

(18)   (19)   (20)

An illustration is given by the reaction of ethyl cyclopropane carboxylate (21) with the strong base triphenylmethyl sodium whereby the ketone (22) is formed rather than a sodium salt. Such a reaction is typical of esters which have no α-hydrogens since, as a rule, esters with an α-hydrogen readily form a sodium salt, i.e. (23)→(24).

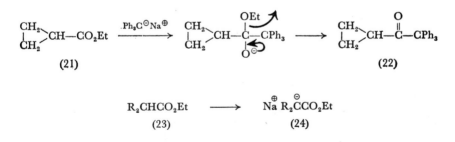

(21)   (22)

$$R_2CHCO_2Et \longrightarrow \overset{\oplus}{Na}\ R_2\overset{\ominus}{C}CO_2Et$$

(23)   (24)

In Chapter 1 (p. 6) we briefly considered one example of a kinetically determined process, namely the solvolysis of cycloalkyl tosylates, and indicated that since the transition state of such a reaction is essentially trigonal the solvolysis of small ring tosylates should proceed relatively slowly. In agreement cyclopropyl tosylate acetolyses extremely slowly, giving, as sole product allyl acetate:

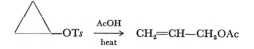

In contrast cyclobutyl tosylate solvolyses at an anomalously high rate comparable with that for cyclopentyl tosylate; the special factors involved here will be considered later on in this chapter.

A reaction series in which the cyclobutyl derivative adopts a position more in line with that expected from angle strain considerations is found in the rates of hydrolysis of ketals of cyclic ketones:

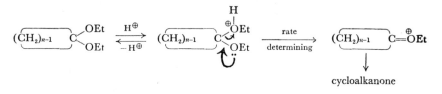

Here the rate determining step involves a reduction in coordination number at a ring carbon from four to three. The rate constant for the cyclobutyl derivative relative to cyclohexyl $= 1$ is 0.0142.

One other rate controlled reaction which fits the general scheme in the case of small ring compounds is the rates of S_N2 displacement at a ring carbon atom. Thus both cyclopropyl and cyclobutyl bromide react more slowly with potassium iodide in acetone than does isopropyl bromide; this is probably a consequence of the increased angle strain associated with the central trigonal carbon atom in the transition state of an S_N2 reaction:

$$I^\ominus + \underset{|}{\overset{|}{>}}C\!-\!Br \longrightarrow \left[I\text{-}\text{-}\text{-}\overset{|}{\underset{|}{C}}\text{-}\text{-}Br\right]^\ominus \longrightarrow I\!-\!\overset{|}{\underset{|}{C}}< + \ Br^\ominus$$

Conjugation involving a Cyclopropane Ring. One of the familiar properties of a double bond is that of conjugation with other π-electron systems, and this is usually considered to involve overlap of the π-electrons of the double bond with those of the conjugating group. As shown in (25) for the case of an $\alpha\beta$-unsaturated ketone, maximum overlap occurs when the π-orbitals are parallel, i.e. when the atoms of the double bond and carbonyl group are in the same plane.

Physical evidence for such conjugation in the ground state of unsaturated ketones comes from a lowering of the frequency of the carbonyl

38

stretching band in the infrared. Thus, whereas a non-conjugated ketone absorbs at 1720 cm.$^{-1}$ an $\alpha\beta$-unsaturated ketone absorbs in the region 1665–1685 cm.$^{-1}$. In valence-bond terms, conjugation may be expressed as a contribution to the resonance hybrid of the dipolar form (27). The lowering of the frequency of the carbonyl stretching band on conjugation with a double bond may then be ascribed to a diminished force constant of the C—O bond due to the contribution of canonical form (27).

$$\left[\begin{array}{c} \overset{\displaystyle >}{}C{=}\overset{|}{C}{-}\overset{|}{C}{=}O \\ \updownarrow \\ \overset{\displaystyle >}{}\overset{\oplus}{C}{-}\overset{|}{C}{=}\overset{|}{C}{-}\overset{\ominus}{O} \end{array} \right] \quad \begin{array}{c} (26) \\ \\ (27) \end{array}$$

(25)

Evidence for conjugation in the excited state of $\alpha\beta$-unsaturated ketones comes from their electronic spectra. Isolated double bonds strongly absorb ultraviolet light at wavelengths below 2000 Å and this absorption corresponds to the excitation of one of the two electrons in the π-orbital into an antibonding π-orbital. When a double bond and a carbonyl group are conjugated the energy of the antibonding orbital is lowered since, broadly speaking, it extends over four instead of two atoms. Thus the electronic transition requires light of lower energy (i.e. longer wavelength). In fact excitation occurs at wavelengths some 300 Å longer than with isolated double bonds. Hence $\alpha\beta$-unsaturated ketones absorb light in the region 2200–2400 Å, the precise wavelength depending on the constitution of the particular compound.

Chemical evidence for conjugation in $\alpha\beta$-unsaturated ketones, i.e. π-overlap in the transition state of a reaction, comes from, for example, the Michael addition reaction (see p. 15). Here, conjugation results in the electron deficiency of the carbonyl carbon atom being relayed to the β-carbon atom.

All the manifestations of conjugation may be diminished or completely eliminated if, for steric reasons, the double bond and carbonyl group are prevented from being coplanar. The latter phenomenon is known as steric inhibition of conjugation.

We have already seen that the orbitals forming the C—C bonds of cyclopropane have high p-character. Thus it might be anticipated that conjugation of a cyclopropane ring with, for example, a carbonyl group might occur, thereby providing yet another analogy between a double bond and a cyclopropane ring. Here the preferred geometrical arrangement for conjugation would be that with the plane of the cyclopropane ring at right angles to the plane of the carbonyl group. This should give maximum overlap of the p-type orbitals of the ring with the π-orbitals of the carbonyl group. Any forcible distortion of the system away from this preferred relationship will result in a reduction in conjugation effects. Suitably constituted cyclopropyl ketones do show conjugation; e.g. methyl cyclopropyl ketone shows carbonyl absorption in the infrared at 1704 cm.$^{-1}$ and absorbs maximally in the ultraviolet at 206 mμ (ϵ, 1310). The corresponding figures for methyl 2-methylcyclopropyl ketone are 1699 cm.$^{-1}$ and 209·5 mμ (ϵ, 1930). Ultraviolet spectral evidence for conjugation in the excited state between a double bond and a cyclopropyl ring has also been obtained.

Michael type addition reactions to cyclopropyl ester and ketones are known, as, for example:

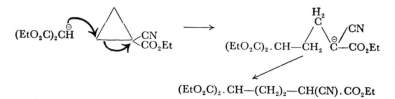

In the case of the unsaturated cyclopropyl ester (28) both 1,4- and 1,6-conjugate addition occur:

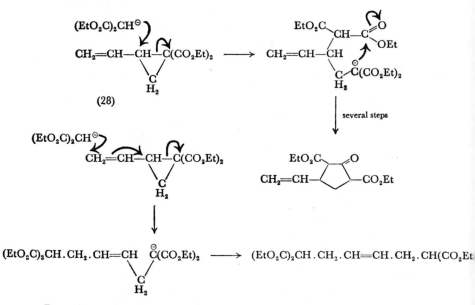

Reactions of the above type are sometimes considered to be chemical evidence for conjugative interactions involving a cyclopropane ring in the transition state.

40

The Dipole Moments of Cycloalkyl Bromides. One further physical characteristic which emphasizes the similarity between a double bond and a cyclopropane ring is the dipole moments of the cycloalkyl bromides. The following values (in Debyes) are found: cyclopropyl bromide, 1·69; cyclobutyl bromide, 2·09; cyclopentyl bromide, 2·16; and cyclohexyl bromide, 2·31. Thus the dipole moment of cyclopropyl bromide is much lower than that of the others and much closer to that of vinyl bromide (1·48). The low dipole moment of vinyl bromide is considered to be a result of the greater electronegativity of an sp^2 hybridized carbon atom compared with an sp^3 carbon atom. Here again, therefore, we have evidence that the hybridization of the carbon atoms in cyclopropane is somewhere between sp^2 and sp^3.

Cyclopropene and its Derivatives. One small ring compound which is of especial interest is cyclopropene (30). This amazing molecule, which clearly possesses a high degree of bond angle strain, was, in fact, prepared many years ago by Demjanov by a Hofmann elimination reaction on the quaternary ammonium hydroxide (29). Cyclopropene and cyclopropyldimethylamine (31) are obtained in about equal amounts.

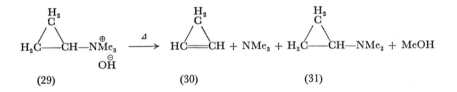

(29)   (30)   (31)

From the theoretical point of view cyclopropene is a very interesting compound. The double bond of cyclopropene is expected to be very reactive towards addition reactions since this would result in a release of some of the bond angle strain. Furthermore, if the analogy between an olefinic bond and cyclopropane is extended, we might expect some similarities between cyclopropene and acetylene. Thus the orbitals forming the vinyl C—H bonds in cyclopropene are expected to have greater s-character than 'normal' vinyl C—H bonds and the double bond carbon atoms should be more electronegative than those of, e.g., ethylene. This leads to the expectation that the olefinic C—H stretching bands of cyclopropene should be at abnormally high frequencies, and that the vinyl hydrogens should be acidic, rather like an acetylenic hydrogen. As we shall see in the sequel these predictions are, in fact, borne out by experience.

Cyclopropene is stable indefinitely at liquid nitrogen temperature but polymerizes rapidly and spontaneously at room temperature. On heating

4

in a stream of helium it undergoes smooth isomerization to methyl acetylene:

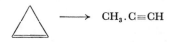

It reacts rapidly with cyclopentadiene at 0° with formation of a Diels-Alder type adduct (32). The ease with which this reaction occurs shows that a considerable amount of strain has already been relieved in the transition state.

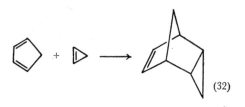

(32)

Two routes which have been employed in the synthesis of cyclo-propenes deserve mention. One is an extension of the addition of car-benes to double bonds (see p. 23) to include acetylenes. Thus addition of methylene, produced photolytically from diazomethane, to but-2-yne (33) gives 1,2-dimethylcyclopropene (34). Similarly but-2-yne and carbethoxycarbene yield ethyl 1,2-dimethylcyclopropene-3-carboxylate (35).

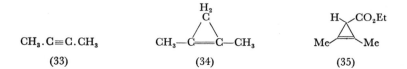

$CH_3.C\equiv C.CH_3$ 　　　$CH_3-C=\!\!\!=\!\!\!C-CH_3$ 　　　

(33) 　　　　　　　　(34) 　　　　　　　(35)

Such substituted cyclopropenes are more stable than cyclopropene itself, e.g., dimethylcyclopropene (34) does not polymerize at 0°.

The above procedure has been applied to the synthesis of the one known naturally occurring cyclopropene, sterculic acid (37), by addition of methylene to stearolic acid (36).

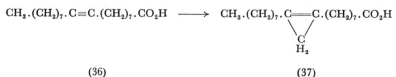

$CH_3.(CH_2)_7.C\equiv C.(CH_2)_7.CO_2H \longrightarrow CH_3.(CH_2)_7.C=\!\!\!=\!\!\!C.(CH_2)_7.CO_2H$

(36) 　　　　　　　　　　　　　　　(37)

The other general route to cyclopropenes involves the intramolecular addition of an allylic carbene to its own double bond. The appropriate carbene is accessible by alkaline decomposition of the *p*-toluenesulphonylhydrazone of an αβ-unsaturated aldehyde, e.g., (38), which affords the carbene (39), rearrangement of which gives the trimethylcyclopropene (40). Breakdown of the tosylhydrazone (38) can be envisaged as occurring by way of the diazocompound which decomposes thermally to the carbene:

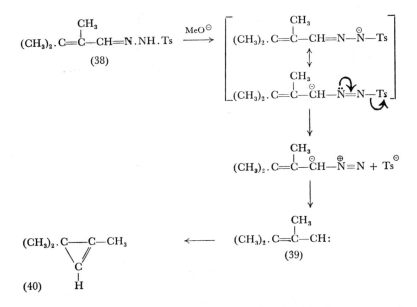

The cyclopropene (40) is of interest since the vinyl hydrogen atom has been shown to be sufficiently acidic to be metallated by butyl lithium, giving (41), thereby justifying expectations. That metallation has taken place as shown is demonstrated by carboxylation of (41) to the acid (42)

Cyclopropenium Compounds. Certain cyclopropene derivatives are of particular interest in connection with theories of 'aromaticity'. One of the consequences of E. Hückel's pioneering molecular orbital calculations on aromatic systems is that a large 'resonance energy' should be associated with cyclic fully conjugated π-electron systems containing

43

$(4n+2)$ π-electrons, where n is any integer. When $n = 1$, there are 6 π-electrons; the best-known aromatic systems such as benzene, tropylium cation and cyclopentadienyl anion possess this 'sextet' of π-electrons. The simplest of such systems would, therefore, be that with $n = 0$ and hence possessing 2 π-electrons, these requirements would be satisfied by a cyclopropene ring bearing a positive charge, i.e. a 'hybrid' of the 'Kekulé' type structures (43–45). Such an ion could be represented by (46).

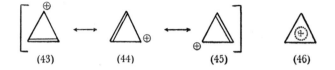

Several compounds of this structural type have, in fact, been prepared as stable salts reminiscent of the tropylium salts. For example, the reaction of benzal chloride and potassium t-butoxide with diphenylacetylene gives the t-butyl ether (47), which on cleavage with hydrogen bromide is converted into the salt triphenylcyclopropenium bromide (48). In this reaction benzal chloride and potassium t-butoxide give first phenyl-chlorocarbene, which then adds to diphenylacetylene; the triphenyl-cyclopropenyl chloride thus formed is subsequently attacked by t-butoxide ion to give the ether (47):

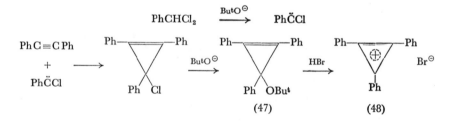

The full implications of this result cannot be discussed here, but the preparation of such cyclopropenium salts seems to be a clear vindication of Hückel's theory. The stabilization of the cyclopropenium ion must be considerable since coordination with the halide ion would relieve angle strain due to the trigonal atom; thus the decrease in energy from the fully delocalized ion must more than outweight the increased angle strain.

Analogy with tropone (49) and extension of the above reasoning leads to the suggestion that the ketone derived from cyclopropene, cyclopropenone, should also be stable, in contrast to cyclopropanone itself. Diphenylcyclopropenone (51) has been prepared by acid hydrolysis of the adduct (50) from dichlorocarbene and diphenylacetylene. Just as

44

with tropone, diphenylcyclopropenone is basic and can be extracted from organic solvents using fairly strong mineral acids due to formation of the conjugate acid (52)

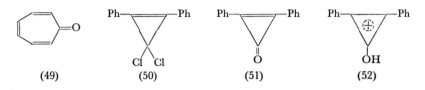

| (49) | (50) | (51) | (52) |

Special Properties of Cyclobutyl Compounds. Many of the reactions of cyclobutane and its derivatives need not be elaborated here because they proceed as expected for cyclic compounds possessing a fair degree of angle strain. Much of the interest associated with the four-membered ring has centered round cyclobutadiene and related compounds. Cyclobutadiene has long been considered as a possible candidate for entry into the select group of non-benzenoid aromatic compounds since it would be a cyclic conjugated polyolefin. However, the theory of Hückel, mentioned above, as well as more sophisticated treatments of the molecule, lead to the expectation of low stability. Thus it is not surprising that many attempts to prepare cyclobutadiene proved abortive. However, a new outlook on cyclobutadiene originated from the fruitful idea, due to L. E. Orgel and H. C. Longuet-Higgins, that cyclobutadiene could be stabilized by coordination with a metal ion (53). Since then both cyclobutadiene and tetramethylcyclobutadiene have been obtained as their silver nitrate complexes and several organometallic compounds derived from cyclobutadiene have been described.

Other derivatives of cyclobutane which have been investigated in connection with the cyclobutadiene problem include cyclobutenones of the type (54), which show no tendency to enolize, and the diketone (55), which has been named phenylcyclobutadienoquinone and is more stable

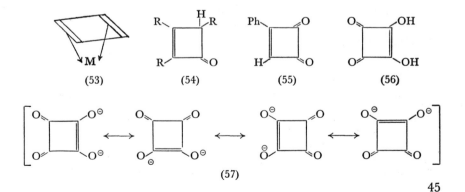

(53)   (54)   (55)   (56)

(57)

45

than *o*-benzoquinone. Among compounds of this category the enol (56) is particularly interesting since it is a fairly strong acid with a pK_2 of 2·2; this is a consequence of the high stability of the highly symmetrical di-anion which may be represented as a resonance hybrid (57).

Interconversions of Cyclobutyl, Cyclopropylcarbinyl and Allylcarbinyl Compounds. When we discussed the relative reactivity of cyclic tosylates in solvolysis reactions it was noticed that cyclobutyl tosylate acetolyses at an anomalously high rate, comparable to that of cyclopentyl tosylate. On the basis of angle strain considerations we would have expected a much slower reaction. Investigation of the products of the acetolysis of cyclobutyl tosylate shows that rearrangement accompanies solvolysis giving cyclopropyl carbinyl acetate (58) and allyl-carbinyl acetate (59) in addition to cyclobutyl acetate

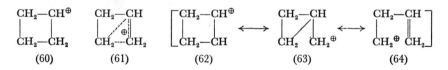

(58) (59)

The anomalous reactivity of cyclobutyl tosylate on acetolysis is considered to be due to electronic reorganization occurring in the rate determining step so that instead of a 'classical' cyclobutyl carbonium ion (60) being formed, the 'non-classical'* ion (61), in which the positive charge is delocalized over three carbon atoms, is obtained. Where delocalization of bonding electrons in a rate determining step results in a rate of ionization higher than that which would otherwise be expected, such a reaction is said to be *anchimerically accelerated*.

For some purposes the non-classical ion (61) may be regarded as a hybrid of the canonical forms (62–64).† Written in this way we can see how coordination of solvent with the centres of positive charge in the intermediate ion can give rise to the respective products. Since the reaction of a carbonium ion with solvent is a highly exothermic reaction the actual distribution of products should represent, to a first approximation, the relative distribution of the positive charge in the intermediate non-classical ion.

$$
\begin{array}{ccccc}
CH_2-CH^{\oplus} & CH_2-CH & \left[CH_2-CH^{\oplus}\right. & CH_2-CH & \left.CH_2-CH\right] \\
| \quad\quad | & |\quad {}_{\oplus}{}^{\|} & | \quad\quad | & | \quad \diagup & | \quad\quad \| \\
CH_2-CH_2 & CH_2---CH_2 & \left[CH_2-CH\right. & CH_2 \quad CH_2^{\oplus} & \left.CH_2^{\oplus} \quad CH_2\right] \\
(60) & (61) & (62) & (63) & (64)
\end{array}
$$

---

* A 'non-classical' ion differs from a 'classical' ion by virtue of having its charge distributed over more than one atom by delocalization of σ-bonding electrons.

† For further discussion of this point in another instance see Chapter 5, p. 86.

We might expect that the intermediate ion (61) could just as well be formed from cyclopropylcarbinyl tosylate or allylcarbinyl tosylate. In fact, acetolysis of these tosylates gives the same products as obtained from cyclobutyl tosylate.

Closer examination of reactions of this type by J. D. Roberts and co-workers using ¹⁴C labelled starting materials has led to the discovery of further complexities. In this instance the carbonium ion intermediates were produced by deamination of the appropriate amine using nitrous acid. Thus a ¹⁴C-cyclopropylcarbinylamine (65) gave a mixture of cyclobutanol (48%), cyclopropylcarbinol (47%), and allylcarbinol (5%). If the intermediate ion (61), i.e. (66) when labelled, is involved in the reaction, the radioactivity in the product alcohols should be distributed as shown in (67) for the cyclobutanol and (68) for the cyclopropylcarbinol.

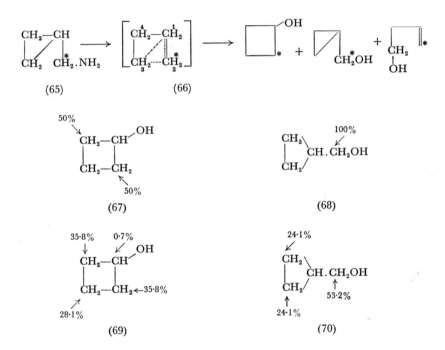

Degradation of the labelled cyclobutanol and cyclopropylcarbinol gave, in fact, the values shown in (69) and (70) respectively. This result indicates that a considerable amount of radioactivity is being shuffled into the methylene groups $C_{(3)}$ and $C_{(4)}$ in (66). As explanation it is proposed that the initially formed ion (66) is converted into the isomeric*

---

* These ions are, of course, only isomeric by virtue of their isotopic distribution.

ions (71) and (72). A possible representation for the transition state or intermediate in the interconversion of the ions is shown in (73).

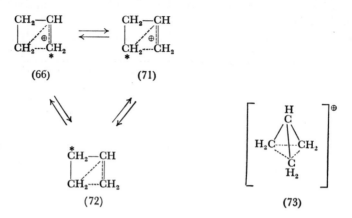

If complete equilibration by way of the ions (66), (71) and (72) were occurring then the cyclobutanol and the cyclopropylcarbinol should be labelled as in (74) and (75) respectively. The discrepancy between these values and the distribution actually found is taken to mean that complete equilibration between the ions does not occur. Thus in formation of the cyclobutanol, 84% (3 × 28) is derived from ions which have undergone equilibration and the remaining 16% is formed directly from the first formed ion (66). On this latter basis the expected distribution of radioactivity in the cyclopropylcarbinol is as in (76). The difference between (76) and the experimentally determined values (70) is considered to mean that about 16% of the cyclopropylcarbinol is formed by a direct S_N2 type reaction leading to unrearranged material with ¹⁴C at the α-carbon atom only.

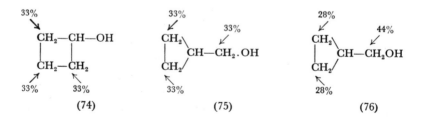

Despite the complexity of this interpretation it does seem to be a satisfactory explanation of the results; these reactions have been discussed in some detail since they provide a good example of the way in which ¹⁴C labelling techniques have led to a better understanding of reaction mechanisms.

Suggestions for Further Reading (Chapter 3)

1. E. VOGEL, 'Small Ring Compounds', in *Fortschritte der Chemischen Forschung*, Vol. 3, p. 430, 1955—this article provides a detailed survey of the preparation and properties of small ring compounds.
2. E. VOGEL, 'Small Ring Compounds', *Angewandte Chemie*, 1960, **72**, 4—a progress report on recent developments subsequent to the first review.
3. J. D. ROBERTS *et al.*, *J. Amer. Chem. Soc.*, 1959, **81**, 4390—a definitive paper giving full details of work on the cyclopropylcarbinyl-cyclobutyl-allylcarbinyl inter-conversions.

CHAPTER 4

NORMAL RINGS—CONFORMATIONAL ANALYSIS

In the so-called normal rings classical Baeyer strain plays only a minor role and models can be built up with preservation of the tetrahedral angle. Such models possess a certain degree of flexibility and a number of fundamentally different forms of the same molecule may be derived merely by rotation about carbon–carbon bonds or by 'flipping'. These forms or _conformations_ will often differ in energy and it is clearly of importance, for a detailed understanding of the chemistry of normal rings, to determine which conformation is the most stable one. This process is usually known as _conformational analysis_; its development is associated particularly with the name of D. H. R. Barton. The energy barriers between different conformations are not usually high enough to allow the separation of pure conformational isomers at room temperature. A familiar example of a case where such a separation _is_ possible is provided by the resolvability of certain diphenyl derivatives.

The discussion will be confined mainly to cyclohexane derivatives, as these have provided most examples of the application of conformational analysis. However, some consideration will first be given to a simple acyclic system to focus attention on the importance of interactions between non-bonded atoms.

n-Butane. If the distance between two non-bonded atoms in a given molecule is less than the sum of their van der Waals radii, strong repulsive interactions will be set up. In the most stable conformation of a molecule the atoms are as far apart as possible, since under these circumstances non-bonded repulsive interactions are at a minimum. The application of this simple concept may be illustrated by the classical case of n-butane, which was first studied by K. S. Pitzer.

A three-dimensional representation of one conformation of the n-butane molecule is shown in (1).* The torsion (projected) angle between the $C_{(1)}$—$C_{(2)}$ and the $C_{(3)}$—$C_{(4)}$ bonds is 180° and any non-bonded repulsive interactions between the two bulky methyl groups are clearly

---

* Two differing methods of three-dimensional representation have been employed here. The upper formulae (a) show a perspective view looking down on the molecule with $C_{(2)}$ in front of $C_{(3)}$. The lower formulae (b) schematically show the situation viewed along the $C_{(2)}$—$C_{(3)}$ bond; the nearer $C_{(2)}$ atom is represented as a point and the distant $C_{(3)}$ atom as a circle. Where the latter method would result in the superposition of bonds the conformation is slightly displaced to 'reveal' the hidden atoms, e.g. (2b) and (4b).

minimized. Conformation (1) is now known as the *anti-periplanar* conformation of n-butane though sometimes the older term *staggered* is used.

If $C_{(3)}$ is kept fixed and $C_{(2)}$ rotated in a clockwise direction about the $C_{(2)}$—$C_{(3)}$ bond through 60°, a situation is reached as shown in (2), the *anti-clinal* conformation. This conformation has a higher energy than conformation (1) due to the increased non-bonded interactions between the methyl groups and the opposed hydrogen atoms. As rotation is continued the methyl–hydrogen interactions are reduced until, after a further 60°, the situation in (3) obtains. This *syn-clinal* or, as it used to be known, *skew or gauche* conformation is of higher energy than (1) due to greater repulsions between the large methyl groups. Rotation through a further 60° leads to the *syn-periplanar* or *eclipsed* conformation (4) which is

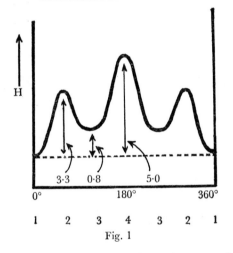

Fig. 1

clearly of higher energy than any other form since non-bonded repulsion between the two methyl groups is at a maximum. Further rotation leads, in reverse, to the situations already considered. The relationship between the torsion angle and energy of the system is shown in Fig. 1. Approximate energy* differences in kcal./mole relative to the most stable conformation (1) are shown.

The above energy values mean that statistically about 19% of the molecules of n-butane have a conformation approximating to (3), the remainder being in the most stable conformation (1). Other conformations account for less than three-tenths of a percent of the total molecules.

Cyclohexane. In the early part of this century Sachse and Mohr realized that cyclohexane rings can exist in puckered forms, which are free from angle strain, and they recognized the existence of two forms now known as the *chair* (5) and *boat* (6) conformations of cyclohexane.

* Strictly speaking we are referring here to enthalpy (H) values.

51

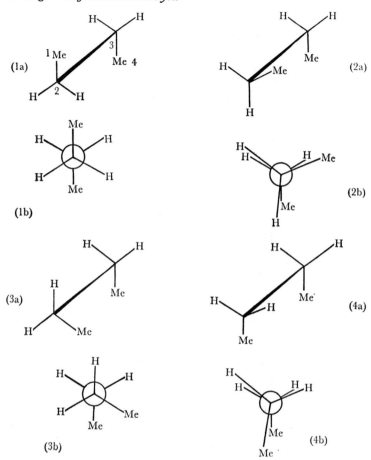

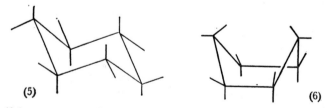

Clearly, on the basis of our experience with n-butane the chair conformation of cyclohexane with its more perfectly staggered array of atoms should be more stable than the boat conformation.*

* Thus if the arrangement of atoms round each of the six carbon–carbon bonds of cyclohexane are taken in turn and considered as butane conformations, the chair conformation (5) is seen to be comprised of six syn-clinal partial butane conformations (3). Similarly the boat conformation (6) is made up of four syn-clinal (3) and two syn-periplanar (4) partial butane conformations. Hence the boat conformation should be of higher energy than the chair conformation by approximately $(4 \times 0\cdot8 + 2 \times 5\cdot0) - (6 \times 0\cdot8) = 8\cdot4$ kcal./mole.

Closer examination of a model of the chair conformation of cyclohexane reveals that the attached hydrogen atoms fall into two groups of six: (a) those joined by bonds which are parallel to the axis of the molecule, termed *axial* bonds (7), and (b) those joined by bonds which extend out radially from the axis termed *equatorial* bonds (8).*

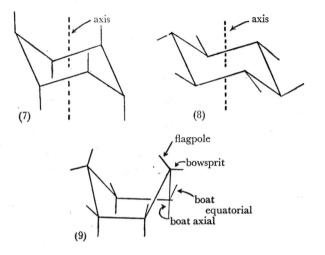

In the boat conformation of cyclohexane the bonds linking the hydrogen atoms to the 'prow' of the boat have been termed, by obvious nautical analogy, *flagpole* and *bowsprit* bonds. The other four pairs of bonds are divided into four *boat equatorial* and four *boat axial* bonds (9).

It has been realized for some time that the 'classical' boat conformation for cyclohexane, as represented in (9), would be considerably destabilized by non-bonded interactions between the 'flagpole' hydrogen atoms, which are only about 1·85 Å apart. However, a characteristic property of the boat conformation of cyclohexane, which is readily apparent from Dreiding models, is that it is highly flexible—in contrast to the relative rigidity of the chair conformation. By simple rotation about carbon–carbon bonds the flagpole hydrogen interactions can be reduced giving a skewed boat conformation which is intermediate between two 'classical' boats. This *skew* or *twist* conformation is the most stable of the *flexible*† conformations of cyclohexane.

One three-dimensional representation of the twist boat conformation of cyclohexane is shown in (11) and its relationship to the 'classical' boat

* Thus *cis* bonds on the same side of the ring are alternately axial and equatorial as one proceeds round the cyclohexane ring. Also, due to the geometry of the ring, the equatorial bond on, for example, $C_{(1)}$ is parallel to the $C_{(2)}$—$C_{(3)}$ and the $C_{(5)}$—$C_{(6)}$ bonds of the ring.

† The term *flexible* may be conveniently used to describe the whole family of conformations of cyclohexane which are related to the boat.

conformation may perhaps be better understood by reference to the two extreme boats (10) and (12); (11) is the half-way stage in the conversion of (10) into (12). An alternative aspect of the twist boat conformation is seen in (13).

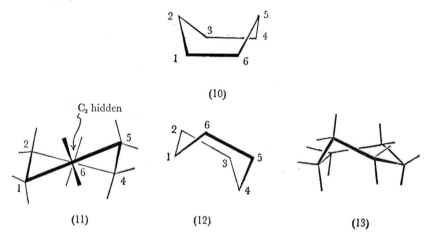

(10)

(11)   (12)   (13)

Fig. 2 gives a rough representation of the conformational energy situation for cyclohexane; it approximates to the energy profile for the conversion of one chair conformation into the other. Thus (b) and (d) are highly strained transition states between the chair (a) and (e) and the twist boat (c)* conformations. In the overall change from (a) to (e) all the axially bonded hydrogen atoms have become equatorial and vice-versa. The enthalpy barrier for the chair–chair interconversion of cyclohexane is about 11 kcal./mole; the twist boat conformation is some 5 kcal./mole less stable than the chair conformation, the extreme boat being about 1·6 kcal./mole of higher energy.

There are two main consequences of the above energy relationships. Firstly, the barrier to interconversion of the two chair conformations of cyclohexane is not sufficiently large to prevent it occurring at room temperature. Secondly, the energy difference between the twist boat and the chair conformation means that for cyclohexane only about 1 molecule in 10,000 is in the twist boat conformation at room temperature.

Monosubstituted Cyclohexanes. For a monosubstituted cyclo-hexane, e.g., methyl cyclohexane, the two chair conformations corre-sponding to (a) and (e) of Fig. 2 are no longer equivalent. One of these has the methyl group in an equatorial position (14) and the other in an axial position (15). These two conformations are, therefore, of different energy; inspection of scale models shows that in the axial conformation (15) the

* For simplicity (c) is drawn as an extreme boat.

methyl group is subject to non-bonded repulsive interactions with the axial hydrogens on $C_{(3)}$ and $C_{(5)}$ These 1,3-axial non-bonded interactions correspond to interactions of the syn-clinal butane type and thus are destabilizing to the extent of about $2 \times 0.8 = 1.6$ kcal./mole. Such interactions are not present in the alternative chair conformation (14) which

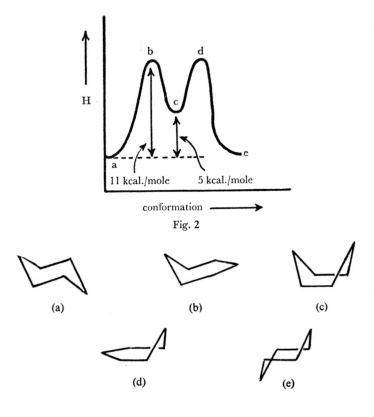

Fig. 2

is, therefore, predicted to be the more stable conformation of methyl cyclohexane.

The energy situation for methyl cyclohexane will thus be approximately as shown in Fig. 3. Again the twist boat conformation will be considerably less stable than either of the two chair conformations and it can be regarded as an unimportant contributor to the population of the ground state at room temperature. The relative importance of the two chair conformations for any particular monosubstituted cyclohexane will depend on the energy difference (ΔH in Fig. 3) in each specific case. Rough experimental measurements of this energy difference have been derived in a number of cases and, from the method of derivation, these are

55

conveniently listed as free energy differences (ΔF)* rather than enthalpy differences. The free energy difference between the two chair conformations of a monosubstituted cyclohexane is found to increase with the steric bulk of the substituent. This is in agreement with the idea that the destabilizing factor associated with an axial substituent is due to repulsive 1,3-interactions with axial hydrogens. For example, for methylcyclohexane $\Delta F = 1\cdot8$ kcal./mole while for t-butylcyclohexane $\Delta F = 5\cdot4$

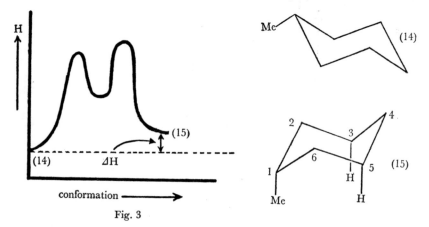

Fig. 3

kcal./mole. Thus in methylcyclohexane about 5% of the molecules are in the chair conformation with an axial methyl group at room temperature. In t-butylcyclohexane, on the other hand, only about one molecule in 10,000 will have an axial t-butyl group; it can, therefore, be said to exist virtually exclusively in the chair conformation with the t-butyl group equatorial.

Disubstituted Cyclohexanes. There are seven possible isomers of a disubstituted cyclohexane. These are: the 1,1-disubstituted isomer, which need not concern us here, and the 1,2-, 1,3-, and 1,4-isomers, each of which can have either a *cis*- and *trans*-configuration.† The latter six possibilities are illustrated for the case of the dimethyl cyclohexanes, the planar representation (upper row) and both of the possible chair conformations being depicted for each (See pages 58 and 59).

Considering for the moment only the chair conformations (justifiable where the substituents are of moderate bulk only [see below]) and

---

* This also has the advantage that the equilibrium constant (K) can be readily calculated using the relationship:

$$\Delta F = -RT \ln K.$$

† It is most important to distinguish clearly between the terms *conformation* and *configuration*; thus (16a) and (17a) are two different configurations of 1,2-dimethylcyclohexane, while (17b) and (17c) are two different *conformations* of *trans*-1,2-dimethylcyclohexane.

utilizing the general principle that a substituent in an axial position will suffer destabilizing interactions, the following conclusions can be drawn: (i) for a *cis*-1,2-disubstituted cyclohexane the two chair conformations (16b) and (16c) are equivalent if the substituents are the same; if the substituents are different, that conformation will predominate which has the bulkier group in the equatorial position. (ii) For a *trans*-1,2-disubstituted cyclohexane the di-equatorial conformation (17b) will be strongly favoured over the alternative diaxial conformation (17c). (iii) If equilibrium between the *cis*- and *trans*-isomers of a 1,2-disubstituted cyclohexane can be established then the *trans*-isomer will predominate since it can exist in the more stable conformation (17b) with no axial substituents.

Inspection of the chair conformations of the 1,3- and 1,4-disubstituted cyclohexanes shows that the *trans*-1,3-compounds (19b and 19c) and the *cis*-1,4-compounds (20b and 20c) disubstituted cyclohexanes are analogous to a *cis*-1,2 disubstituted cyclohexane in having one axial and one equatorial substituent, while the *cis*-1,3-compounds (18b and 18c) and the *trans*-1,4-compounds (21b and 21c) are analogous to a *trans*-1,2-disubstituted cyclohexane in having one diaxial conformation and one diequatorial conformation. This leads to the interesting conclusion that if equilibrium between the two 1,3-disubstituted cyclohexanes can be established then the *cis*-isomer should predominate since it can exist in conformation (18b) with both substituents equatorial. This prediction, which is opposed to classical ideas, has been fully substantiated and could not have been made without the aid of conformational analysis.

The large difference in 'steric bulk' between the t-butyl group and most other functional groups is sometimes used as a means of essentially fixing ground state conformations. Thus *cis*- and *trans*-4-t-butylcyclohexanol (22 and 23) are examples of relatively simple cyclohexane derivatives which have purely axial and purely equatorial hydroxyl groups respectively. A number of examples of this use of t-butylcyclohexyl derivatives will be encountered later.

If in a disubstituted cyclohexane both of the substituents are bulky, e.g. a di-t-butylcyclohexane, the assumption that the contribution of flexible conformations is negligible is no longer always justifiable. Thus in the case of *trans*-1,3-di-t-butylcyclohexane, if the ring is to remain in the chair conformation (see conformations 19b and 19c) one of the t-butyl groups must necessarily be in an axial position (24). This, as already discussed, would produce a destabilizing interaction of about 5·4 kcal./mole which could be relieved by conversion of the ring into a flexible conformation. Apparently we have here an example of a substituted cyclohexane for which the preferred conformation is the twist boat conformation.

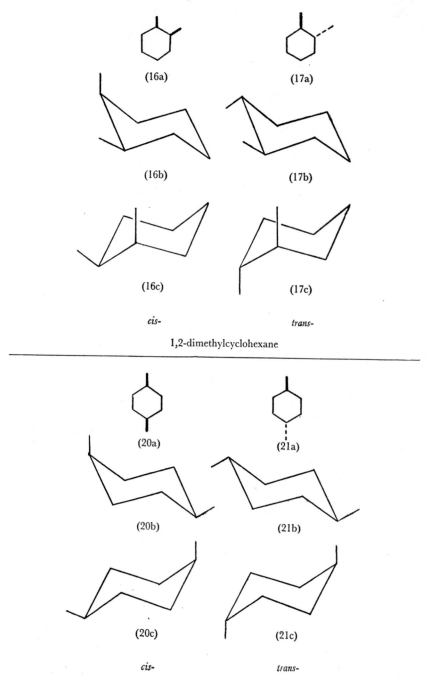

(16a)

(17a)

(16b)

(17b)

(16c)

(17c)

cis-

trans-

1,2-dimethylcyclohexane

(20a)

(21a)

(20b)

(21b)

(20c)

(21c)

cis-

trans-

1,4-dimethylcyclohexane

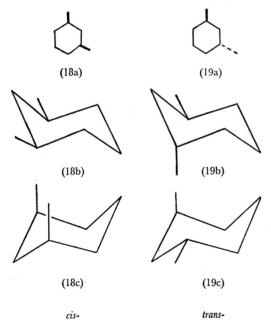

(18a)　　　　　　　　(19a)

(18b)　　　　　　　　(19b)

(18c)　　　　　　　　(19c)

cis-　　　　　　　　*trans-*

1,3-dimethylcyclohexane

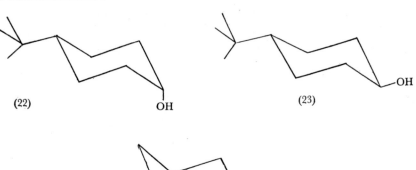

(22)

OH

(23)

OH

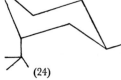

(24)

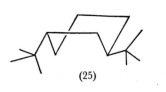

(25)

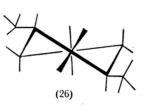

(26)

The preferred twist conformation (26) is the one intermediate between the two extreme boats in which one t-butyl group is in a boat-equatorial position and one is in a bowsprit position, e.g., (25); other twist forms will be destabilized by having one t-butyl group in an approximately boat-axial position.

Polysubstituted Cyclohexanes. These will not be discussed in detail as the situation in each case follows by extrapolation from the ideas already set out. Thus, with the above reservations concerning conformations having large groups in an axial position, the generalization may be made that the preferred conformation of a polysubstituted cyclohexane will be that chair conformation which has the largest number of substituents in equatorial positions.

Anomalies. The generalizations concerning the preferred conformations of cyclohexane derivatives are valid in a large number of cases and in particular where all, or all but one, of the substituents are groups of low polarity, such as alkyl groups. However, there are certain cases where, for example, dipole–dipole interactions or hydrogen bonding can upset the stability order based on predictions which are dependent only on the steric bulk of the substituents. One example of each should suffice as illustrations.

trans-1,2-Dibromocyclohexane would be expected on steric grounds alone to exist almost wholly in the diequatorial chair conformation (27). In fact dipole moment measurements show that conformation (27) is in equilibrium with substantial amounts of the diaxial conformation (28) and that the position of equilibrium is dependent on the solvent used.

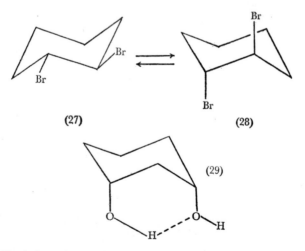

(27)   (28)

(29)

In the diaxial conformation (28) the strong C—Br dipoles are aligned 180° apart so that on electrostatic grounds this conformation will be more stable than the diequatorial one (27) where the C—Br dipoles are only inclined at 60°. Solvents of high dielectric constant can effectively disperse the dipoles by solvation, so that in these solvents the sterically favoured conformation (27) is preferred. On the other hand, in solvents of low dielectric constant, where dipole solvation does not operate, the electrostatically favoured isomer (28) predominates.

cis-Cyclohexane-1,3-diol has been shown by infrared studies to exhibit strong intramolecular hydrogen bonding in dilute carbon tetrachloride solution. Such hydrogen bonding can only occur in the chair conformation with both the hydroxyl groups in an axial position (29). Thus any destabilization due to non-bonded interactions associated with the two axial groups is more than compensated by the gain in energy due to hydrogen bonding.

Cyclohexanone and Cyclohexene. The derivatives of cyclohexane which have so far been considered have all been constructed of tetrahedral ring carbon atoms. When one or more trigonal carbon atoms are introduced into the cyclohexane ring a new situation will obviously arise and each case has to be considered on its merits. Only two such cases will be discussed here, those of cyclohexanone and cyclohexene.

Cyclohexanone (30), with one trigonal carbon atom, is only very slightly distorted from normal cyclohexane geometry. The chief distinction from cyclohexane is the absence of one axial and one equatorial

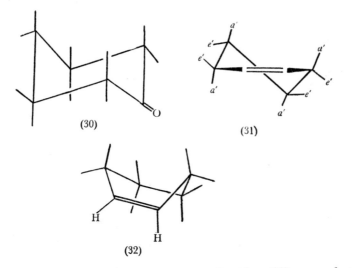

(30)

(31)

(32)

hydrogen atom; this leads to some second order differences between certain substituted cyclohexanones and the corresponding cyclohexanes.

In cyclohexene the two adjacent trigonal carbon atoms of the double bond and the two allylic carbons are constrained to be in a plane. This leads to two conformations for cyclohexene: the '*half-chair*' (31) and the '*half-boat*'* (32). In diagram (31), the half-chair conformation is viewed in the plane of the double bond showing that one carbon atom is above and one is below the plane of the remaining four. The half-boat conformation is not flexible like the boat conformation of cyclohexane and there are only two half-boat conformations in cyclohexene. Interconversion between the two can occur by way of the half-chair as intermediate. Available evidence indicates that, in the absence of special effects, cyclohexene and its derivatives will exist predominantly in the half-chair conformation. In the case of cyclohexene itself the half-chair is calculated to be about 2·7 kcal./mole more stable than the half-boat conformation.

Examination of a scale model of cyclohexene in the half-chair conformation reveals that four hydrogen atoms are in positions which approximate to axial positions—these are termed *quasi-axial* positions (marked a' in 31)—and the other four methylene hydrogens are in *quasi-equatorial* positions (e').

Fused Ring Systems—The Decalins. The fusion of two or more cyclohexane rings can result in a considerable restriction of conformational mobility. This may be illustrated by consideration of the situation in the decalins.

The decalin system, comprising two fused cyclohexane rings, can, of course, exist in two configurations, i.e. *trans*- (33) and *cis*-decalin (34).

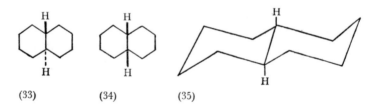

(33)   (34)   (35)

Examination of models shows that only one conformation (35) of *trans*-decalin can be constructed using two chair cyclohexane rings. In this conformation the hydrogen atoms at the ring junctions are axial to both rings. Although one or both of the rings can in principle assume a limited number of flexible conformations (two extreme boats and the intermediate twist-boat), it is to be expected, as in cyclohexane itself, that such conformations will not contribute to the ground state of *trans*-decalin.

The *trans*-decalin skeleton thus offers a convenient means, complementary to the t-butylcyclohexyl system, of ensuring the conformational

---

* In the half-boat conformation of cyclohexene the double bond flattens the ring in comparison with the boat conformation of cyclohexane.

disposition of a substituent. For example, in *trans-cis*-1-decalol (36)* = (37) the hydroxyl group is axial while in *trans-trans*-1-decalol (38) = (39) it is equatorial.

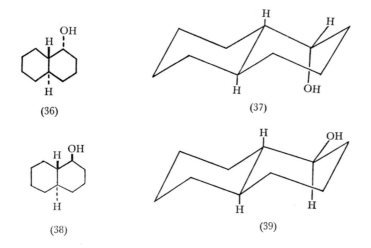

(36)

(37)

(38)

(39)

When we come to consider the model of *cis*-decalin it emerges that two equivalent all-chair conformations can be constructed. Here the hydrogen atoms at the ring junctions are each axial to one ring and equatorial to the other. The two conformations are identical in the case of *cis*-decalin itself but are different in the case of a substituted *cis*-decalin. The two equivalent conformations for *cis*-decalin are shown in (40) and (41) and the corresponding two non-equivalent conformations for a mono-substituted *cis*-decalin are illustrated for *cis-trans*-1-decalol (42) and (43), cf. (44). In conformation (42) the hydroxyl group is equatorial and in (43) it is axial. Interconversion between these two conformations can occur *via* the appropriate flexible conformation (both rings must be in a flexible conformation for this to occur) and the energy barrier of the interconversion is insufficiently high to prevent equilibration at room temperature. The situation is akin to that in a monosubstituted cyclohexane, and the preferred conformation will be that with the equatorial substituent (42).

Closer examination of conformation (42) reveals an interaction between the equatorial hydroxyl and the equatorial hydrogen on $C_{(8)}$. This interaction is equivalent to a 1,3-diaxial interaction so that it should lead to a destabilization of (42) relative to the equatorial conformation of cyclohexanol. Such an additional interaction is absent in (43), thus the

* In specifying the stereochemistry of substituted decalins the first configurational assignment defines the ring junction while the second gives the relationship of the *hydrogen atom* on the substituted carbon, to the closest bridgehead hydrogen.

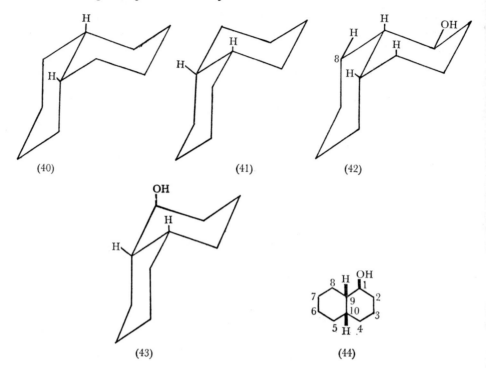

(40)　　　　(41)　　　　(42)

(43)　　　　(44)

free energy difference between conformations (42) and (43) is not expected to be as large as that between the two chair conformations of cyclohexanol. This type of complication does not occur with an equatorial 2-substituted *cis*-decalin.

To illustrate further the complexity of the *cis*-decalin system we may consider the case of *cis-cis*-1-decalol. Here the two possible all-chair conformations are as in (45) and (46) respectively.

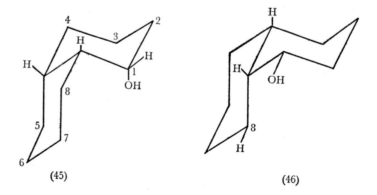

(45)　　　　(46)

64

In conformation (46) the hydroxyl group is equatorial but it suffers the equivalent of a 1,3-diaxial interaction with the equatorial hydrogen on $C_{(8)}$. This conformation should thus be of comparable stability to conformation (42) of *trans-cis*-1-decalol. In the alternative conformation (45) the axial hydroxyl group is placed in a 1,3-diaxial type of relation with respect to the $C_{(7)}$ and $C_{(5)}$ methylene groups. These interactions should strongly destabilize conformation (45) relative to (46).

To summarize: Additional complications can occur in substituted *cis*-decalins due to interaction between the substituents and methylene groups in the other ring.

The next question requiring an answer in connection with *cis*- and *trans*-decalin is: Which of the two isomers is the more stable? In the light of our experience with 1,2-disubstituted cyclohexane derivatives it would be expected that the *trans*-isomer is the more stable. This follows because in *trans*-decalin each ring possesses effectively two equatorial substituents (the adjacent methylene groups of the other ring) while in *cis*-decalin each ring has one equatorial and one axial substituent. This prediction has been verified by equilibration of the two isomers of decalin by heating in the presence of palladium–carbon. At 530° the equilibrium mixture contains 9% *cis*-decalin.

For 9-methyl decalin the energy difference between the isomers is much smaller and the equilibrium mixture of *cis*- and *trans*-9-methyl-decalin, again established using palladium–carbon, contains only 55% of the *trans*-isomer at 584°. This is largely due to the presence, in the *trans*-isomer (47), of two unfavourable interactions between the axial methyl group and the axial hydrogens at $C_{(5)}$ and $C_{(7)}$. These interactions are removed on conversion to the *cis*-isomer (48).

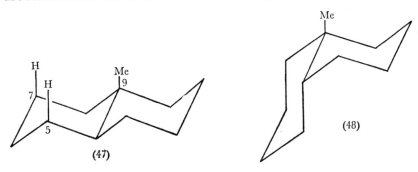

REACTIONS OF CYCLOHEXANE DERIVATIVES

Having surveyed the factors which govern the preferred conformations of cyclohexane derivatives we may now proceed to a consideration of the effect of conformation on reactions. Many of the ideas on this subject

65

were first developed from natural products, such as the steroids and triterpenes, which are essentially fairly rigid polycyclic systems usually of the *trans*-decalin type. Where possible in the ensuing discussion, examples will be chosen from the derivatives of cyclohexane itself, but it will occasionally be necessary to refer to more complex *trans*-decalin types for suitable illustrations. Where this is necessary partial formulae, e.g. (75) and (76), will be used to define the significant part of the molecule.

As usual the discussion is conveniently divided into equilibrium controlled reactions and rate controlled reactions.

Equilibrium Reactions. Since the prediction of the outcome of an equilibrium controlled reaction depends only on the relative stabilities of starting materials and products, the application of conformational principles is fairly straightforward.

We have already mentioned some examples of the palladium–carbon equilibration of isomeric hydrocarbons which occurs at high temperatures. As it is of limited preparative interest it will not be further discussed here.

The most important group of equilibrium reactions involves the interconversion of isomers by way of an enol or of an enolate ion. Thus if two isomers differ only in their configuration about a carbon atom which bears a hydrogen atom and which is adjacent to a carbonyl or similar group, treatment of either isomer with acid or base, under suitable conditions, should result in the establishment of equilibrium between them.

For example, either ethyl *cis*-4-t-butylcyclohexane carboxylate (49), with an axial ethoxycarbonyl group, or its equatorial *trans*-isomer (51) is converted into an equilibrium mixture of the two on heating under reflux with sodium ethoxide in ethanol. The equilibrium mixture contains 84% of the *trans*-isomer, as expected on conformational grounds.

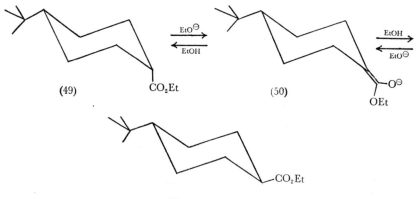

$EtO^{\ominus}$ · EtOH (49) · CO$_2$Et · (50) · EtOH · EtO$^{\ominus}$ · O$^{\ominus}$ · OEt · CO$_2$Et · (51)

In a similar fashion *trans*-2-methyl-4-t-butylcyclohexanone (52) is converted largely into the *cis*-isomer (54), with an equatorial methyl group, on acid or base treatment. The transformation is illustrated for the acid catalysed reaction proceeding through the enol (53). Equilibrium is more readily established here than in the case of the ester due to the faster rate of enolization of a ketone:

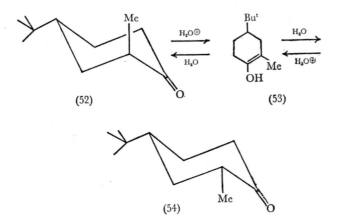

(52) (53)

(54)

Correspondingly *cis*-α-decalone (55) is converted almost entirely into *trans*-α-decalone (56) by base catalysed isomerization. The relative stability is thus that expected from the parent hydrocarbons. With substituted α-decalones, especially 9-methyl-α-decalones where the parent

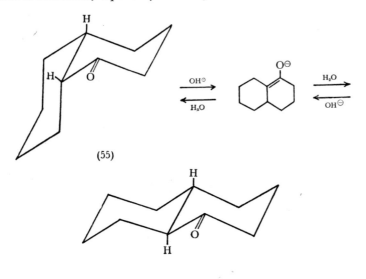

(55)

(56)

67

hydrocarbons differ little in energy, no all embracing generalization can be made and each case needs to be considered on its merits.

Another type of equilibrium reaction commonly encountered is that of epimerization of a secondary hydroxyl group. This occurs under strongly basic conditions and has been shown to involve catalytic quantities of ketonic material:

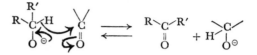

An alternative method consists of heating the secondary alcohol in isopropyl alcohol with aluminium isopropoxide in the presence of a trace of acetone. Under such conditions the isomeric 4-t-butylcyclohexanols can be interconverted. At equilibrium the diequatorial *trans*-isomer (58) predominates, as expected on conformational grounds, and the equilibrium constant (*cis* ⇌ *trans*) is 3·76 at 89° giving $\Delta F = -0.96$ kcal./mole.

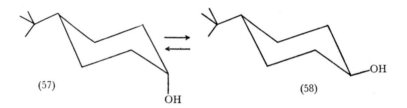

(57)   (58)

OH

Kinetically Controlled Reactions. So far the discussion has been concerned with the preferred ground state conformations of cyclohexane derivatives. When we come to consider a kinetically controlled reaction it is important to realize that the conformation assumed in the transition state need not necessarily be the same as that of the starting state. The energy of activation of most reactions is considerably greater than the energy barrier between conformational isomers. Thus the overall energy of activation of a reaction proceeding through a conformation different from that of the starting state may well be lower than that of reaction *via* the preferred ground state conformation if the less stable conformation better satisfies the electronic requirements of the transition state.

This section will be concerned with a number of examples of reactions whose conformational requirements are reasonably clear. Once again these examples are intended to be illustrative rather than exhaustive.

The reactivity of a cyclohexane derivative may be affected by conformation in two main ways: (i) a reaction involving an axially bonded substituent will usually be more sterically retarded than that involving an equatorial substituent, (ii) certain reactions are found to have particular conformational requirements which put a restriction either (a) on the conformation of the compound undergoing reaction and/or (b) on the nature of the products formed.

(i) *Steric Hindrance of Axial Substituents.* The formation and hydrolysis of esters of substituted cyclohexanols are examples of this type of reaction. In both cases the product-determining intermediate is of the ortho-ester type, e.g. (60) in the case of the saponification of the acetate of a secondary alcohol (59).

$$\underset{\text{(59)}}{\overset{\displaystyle O}{>\!C\!-\!O\!-\!\overset{\|}{C}\!-\!CH_3}} + OH^{\ominus} \underset{K}{\overset{}{\rightleftharpoons}} \underset{\text{(60)}}{\overset{\displaystyle O^{\ominus}}{>\!C\!-\!O\!-\!\overset{|}{\underset{OH}{C}}\!-\!CH_3}} \overset{k}{\longrightarrow}$$

$$\underset{\text{(61)}}{>\!C\!-\!O^{\ominus}} + CH_3 . CO_2H \overset{\text{rapid}}{\longrightarrow} >\!C\!-\!OH + CH_3 . CO_2^{\ominus}$$

Both the equilibrium constant K for formation of the intermediate (60) and the rate constant k for its breakdown to products will be affected by steric hindrance of the carbonyl group in the acetate. In general they will be affected in opposite directions. Thus increased steric hindrance at the carbonyl carbon should decrease K by destabilizing the intermediate but increase k because the step (60) → (61) will then be accompanied by a relief of steric strain. In practice it is found that the former effect dominates so that strictly speaking this is not a kinetically controlled reaction. Thus the acetate, or other ester, of an axial cyclohexanol is usually hydrolysed appreciably more slowly than its equatorial isomer. For example, the rate of saponification of the acid phthalate of the equatorial *trans*-4-t-butylcyclohexanol (58) is about ten times that of the *cis*-(axial)-isomer (57). Rate studies of this type have frequently been used to determine the conformational disposition of a hydroxyl group.

Conversely the esters of equatorial cyclohexanols are generally formed more rapidly than those of the corresponding axial alcohol.

Another type of example, where the situation is somewhat changed, is the rates of oxidation of substituted cyclohexanols to the corresponding ketones. As a general rule axial secondary hydroxyl groups are oxidized more rapidly than their equatorial epimers; e.g. the axial *cis*-4-t-butyl-cyclohexanol is oxidized under standard conditions by chromic acid at about three times the rate of the equatorial isomer. Thus although the oxidation probably proceeds *via* an intermediate chromate ester (62), it appears that in this case the rate determining step of the reaction is the

69

decomposition of this intermediate. In the case of the axial alcohol decomposition of the chromate ester is sterically accelerated.

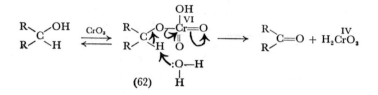

(62)

(ii) *Reactions with Special Conformational Requirements. Elimination Reactions.* Bimolecular elimination reactions, which may be depicted mechanistically as in (63), are a very general type of reaction. Examples include the Hofmann elimination of quaternary ammonium compounds and the base induced elimination of halogen hydracid from an alkyl halide possessing a β-hydrogen. The electronic requirements of this type of reaction demand a so-called *anti-coplanar* arrangement of the proton to be eliminated and the leaving group X. That is, in the terminology introduced in describing the butane conformations, the C—X and the C—H bonds should be anti-periplanar.

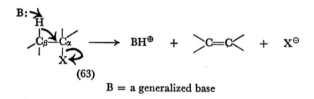

(63)

B = a generalized base

If both C_α and C_β are to be members of a chair cyclohexane ring this anti-periplanar arrangement is only satisfied when the C—H and the C—X bonds are both axial i.e.

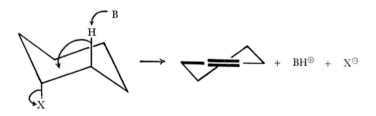

Thus, in the Hofmann elimination of cyclohexyltrimethylammonium hydroxide, the elimination is considered to occur *via* the normally unfavoured conformation in which the trimethylammonium group (comparable in size to a t-butyl group) is in the axial position:

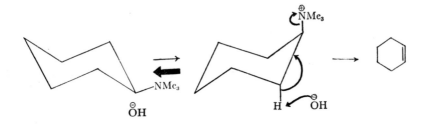

Here we have an example in which the required conformation for the transition state of a reaction is different from the preferred conformation of the starting state.

An instructive example is the ethoxide promoted elimination of hydrogen chloride from neomenthyl chloride (64) and menthyl chloride (65). The preferred conformation of neomenthyl chloride (66), with both the methyl and isopropyl groups equatorial, already has an axial chlorine atom. Thus anti-coplanar elimination of the axial hydrogen atom, either at $C_{(2)}$ or at $C_{(4)}$, can occur. Where such a choice is possible, elimination reactions will tend to lead to the more stable, highly substituted olefin. In this case, therefore, elimination proceeds towards $C_{(4)}$ giving menth-3-ene (67) in about 75% yield and towards $C_{(2)}$ giving menth-2-ene (72) in 25% yield. In menthyl chloride, however, the preferred conformation (68) has an equatorial chlorine and anti-coplanar elimination cannot occur in this conformation. The alternative chair conformation (69) and the twist-boats related to the extreme boat conformations (70) and (71) all possess the right anti-coplanar arrangement, and all are clearly of higher energy than (68). Conformation (71) is probably the least likely candidate as it has both a boat ring and the isopropyl group in a boat-axial position. A decision between the other two cannot readily be made since although (70) is a boat the isopropyl group is in a boat equatorial position while the chair conformation (69) has all three substituents axial. Elimination in one or the other of these conformations leads to the product formed, namely menth-2-ene (72).

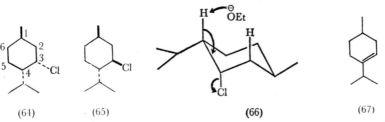

   (64)   (65)   (66)   (67)

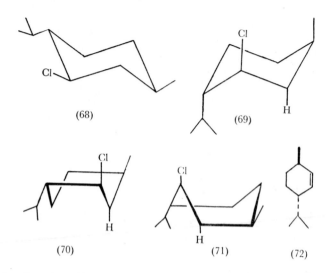

(68)

(69)

(70)

(71)

(72)

Addition Reactions. In a sense many ionic addition reactions to double bonds are effectively the reverse of elimination reactions. Thus, just as bimolecular elimination requires an anti-periplanar relationship between the proton lost and the leaving group, so the addition to a double bond of, e.g., halogen, results in an anti-periplanar arrangement of entering groups. This may be illustrated for the addition of bromine to cyclohexene. Initial attack of bromine on the double bond affords an intermediate bromonium ion which, for present purposes, may be written as in (73) (cf. p. 34). The reaction is completed by displacement by bromide ion as shown, giving initially the diaxial conformation of *trans*-1,2-dibromocyclohexane (74), which is in equilibrium with the diequatorial conformation as previously described.

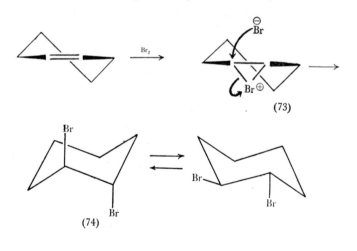

(73)

(74)

Addition of bromine to a conformationally fixed cyclohexene, where final ring inversion cannot occur, results simply in formation of the diaxially substituted dibromide. For a good example of this we need to refer to the bromination of the steroid olefin, partial formula (75), which is essentially a *trans*-decalin derivative. Initial attack of bromine occurs on that face of the olefin opposite to the angular methyl group, which shields attack from above. The resulting bromonium ion (76) could, in principle, be opened by attack of bromide ion either at $C_{(2)}$ or at $C_{(3)}$. However, only attack at $C_{(2)}$ can lead to diaxial dibromide (77), which is the product formed. This transformation is shown both in planar and three-dimensional representations:

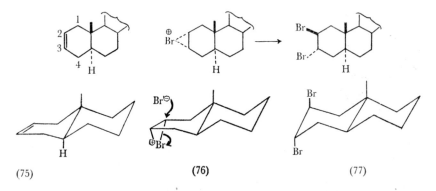

(75)   (76)   (77)

The rule of diaxial addition does not apply to addition of halogen hydracids, e.g. hydrogen bromide, to tri-substituted olefins. Apparently this reaction involves as intermediate the classical carbonium ion produced by proton addition to one terminus of the double bond.

Opening of Epoxide Rings. The opening of epoxide rings is mechanistically similar to the attack of bromide ion on a bromonium ion and again the rule of diaxial opening is usually obeyed. Thus acid catalysed hydrolysis of the epoxide (78), produced by the action of perbenzoic acid on the olefin (75), gives the diaxial glycol (79). Similarly, reduction of the epoxide with lithium aluminium hydride leads to the axial alcohol (80). Here, of course, the entering hydrogen cannot be differentiated from that already present at $C_{(2)}$.

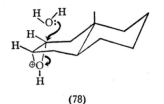

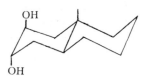

(78)   (79)

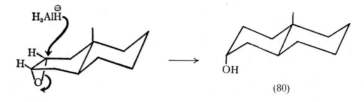

(80)

In the hydrolysis of, e.g., cyclohexene epoxide, diaxial opening is again expected to occur. However, in this flexible system a final chair–chair interconversion can take place to give the most stable conformation of *trans*-cyclohexane-1,2-diol.

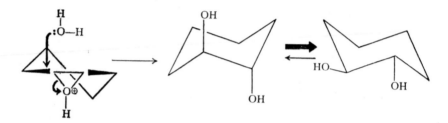

Neighbouring Group Participation. A neighbouring group displacement reaction involves the intramolecular assistance of the ionization of a leaving group Y by a neighbouring group –SA:

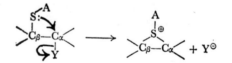

Once again the geometrical requirement for such a reaction is that the C_β–S and C_α–Y bonds should be antiperiplanar, i.e. *trans*-diaxial in a cyclohexane ring.

The now classic example of neighbouring group participation in cyclohexane chemistry is of *trans*-2-acetoxycyclohexyl tosylate (81). The rate of acetolysis of the latter (rate of liberation of *p*-toluene sulphonic acid) is 650 times faster than that of the *cis*-isomer (87 and 88). This is strong evidence that ionization of tosylate ion in the *trans*-isomer occurs with participation of the acetoxyl group in the diaxial conformation (82), giving the intermediate bridged ion (83) directly. The fate of the bridged ion depends on the precise conditions of the experiment; in the presence of water *cis*-cyclohexane-1,2-diol monoacetate (85) is formed *via* the orthomonoacetate (84), while the presence of acetate ion leads to the

74

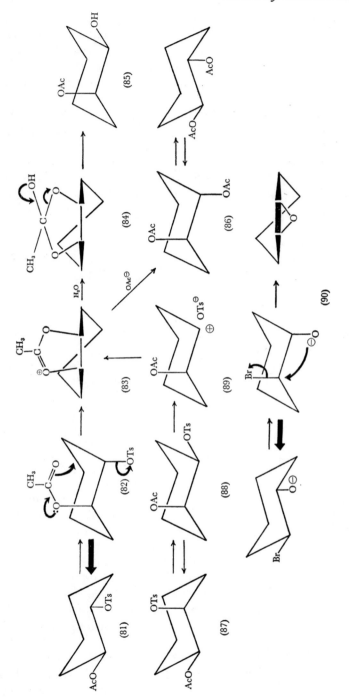

formation of *trans*-cyclohexane-1,2-diol diacetate (86). For *cis*-2-acetoxy-cyclohexyl tosylate (87) the required anti-periplanar arrangement of the C—OTs bond and the C—OAc bond cannot be achieved. Solvolysis occurs therefore by slow rate determining ionization to the classical ion (89) which can then undergo bridging in a subsequent step to give the inter-mediate ion (83).

A simpler example is the formation of cyclohexene epoxide by treat-ment of *trans*-2-bromocyclohexanol, with alkali, a process which involves the conformation (90).

With the isomeric *cis*-2-bromocyclohexanol a completely different reaction occurs; migration of hydrogen with its bonding electrons (hydride shift), results in the formation of cyclohexanone:

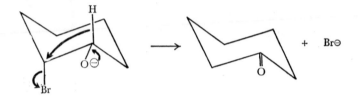

A more complex but instructive example of neighbouring group participation in a cyclohexane ring involves a benzamide group as the neighbouring group and methanesulphonate as the leaving group. Here the immediate product is the heterocyclic cation (91).

The relative rates of reaction of the three substituted cyclohexanes (92), (93) and (94) are respectively 6610, 76 and 260. The high rate in the case of (92) is in agreement with expectation for a compound with axial neighbouring group and leaving group. However, the rate of reaction of (93) is unexpectedly high since the alternative chair conformation with all three substituents, in particular the t-butyl group, axial would be prohibitively destabilized. The most reasonable explanation is that reaction proceeds by way of the twist-boat conformation (95) where essentially the correct orientation of neighbouring group and leaving group is achieved.

This raises the interesting question as to what conformation is assumed by the unsubstituted derivative (94) in the transition state. From the relative rate values, and assuming that the t-butyl group exerts no electronic effect on the reaction, it is concluded that (94) undergoes reaction to the extent of about 70% by way of the alternative chair conformation with both groups axial and to the extent of about 30% by way of the twist-boat conformation corresponding to (95).

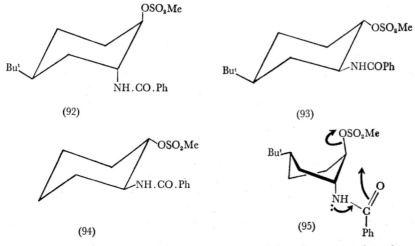

(92)   (93)

(94)   (95)

This detailed investigation of the course of the above reaction shows that many of the generalizations previously made are probably only broadly true. Transition states involving twist forms are likely to be of significance in many cases.

α-Bromination of Ketones. The α-bromination of a ketone involves the enol-form as intermediate. For the bromination of a cyclohexanone the chief point of conformational interest is the preferred orientation of the incoming bromine. This information is frequently obscured by isomerization of the kinetically produced product by subsequent enolization. One way of brominating a ketone under especially mild conditions (thereby preventing equilibration), involves prior conversion of the ketone to the enol-acetate followed by bromination of the latter under buffered conditions. In this way kinetic control of bromination is assured.

To take a more complicated but less ambiguous case first, the *trans-β*-decalone derivative (96), under the above conditions, affords the axial bromoketone (97).

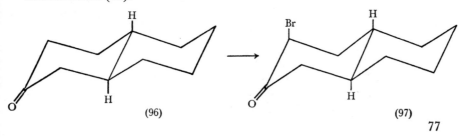

(96)   (97)

77

It thus appears that unhindered bromination of the enol-form of a cyclohexanone results in the axial introduction of the incoming bromine atom. This has been rationalized by the observation that axial bromination ensures maximum overlap of the π-electrons of the enolate system with the electrophilic bromine:

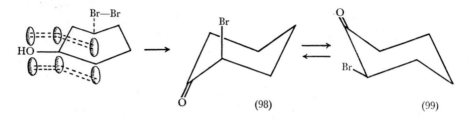

(98)   (99)

With cyclohexanone itself the initially formed axial conformation (98) will be in equilibrium with the equatorial conformation (99). Bromocyclohexanone is another example of a system where the conformational equilibrium position is solvent dependent. In the sterically favoured equatorial conformation (99) the C—Br and C=O dipoles are approximately parallel, which will tend to destabilize this conformation. In a non-polar solvent, e.g. n-heptane, the dipole effect is dominant and the equilibrium mixture contains 85% of conformation (98). The more polar solvent dioxan can partially disperse the dipoles by solvation, and the proportion of the axial isomer drops to about 60%.

Metal Hydride Reduction of Cyclic Ketones. Metal hydride reduction of a cyclohexanone of fixed conformation can, in principle, afford either the equatorial or the axial alcohol (or a mixture of both). In practice the outcome of such a reduction appears to depend on the degree of hindrance of the carbonyl group. Thus relatively non-hindered ketones such as 4-t-butyl cyclohexanone are reduced by lithium aluminium hydride to give predominantly the most stable alcohol, in this case the equatorial *trans*-4-t-butylcyclohexanol:

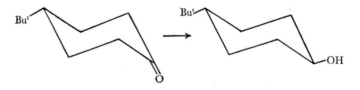

However, with more highly hindered ketones attack of hydride will occur from the less hindered face of the molecule and this frequently leads to the formation of an axial alcohol.

These principles allow us to predict, with reasonable certainty, the course of hydride reduction of ketones; their theoretical basis is insufficiently clear to warrant discussion here.

Rearrangement Reactions. The anti-periplanar arrangement of leaving group and neighbouring group which was found necessary for neighbouring group participation reactions is also mandatory for those rearrangement reactions where, effectively, a carbon–carbon bond is the neighbouring group. This is best discussed with reference to a specific example. Solvolysis of the equatorial tosylate (100) results in ring contraction by way of migration of the bond anti-periplanar to the departing group:

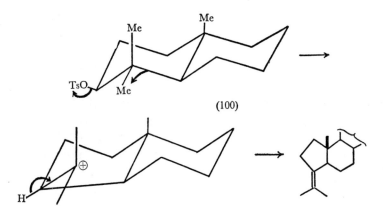

(100)

Conversely, with the axial isomer (101) the anti-periplanar bond is the axial methyl group and thus methyl migration occurs:

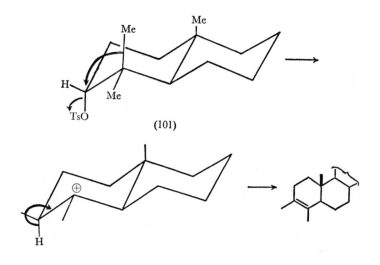

(101)

79

Many examples of the dependence of rearrangement reactions on conformation are known; however, since most of them belong to complex polycyclic compounds of the steroid-triterpene type, they are not properly discussed extensively here.

Cleavage of Cyclohexane-1,2-diols. A familiar reaction of 1,2-diols is their cleavage by lead tetracetate or periodic acid to aldehydes or ketones. This may be illustrated for the case of lead tetra-acetate cleavage of *cis*- or *trans*-cyclohexane-1,2-diol which gives adipic di-aldehyde (103). The rate determining step of this reaction is considered to involve the breakdown of an intermediate lead compound (102).

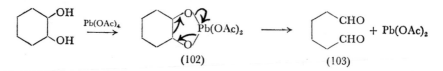

Now it is found experimentally that the *cis*-isomer (104) is cleaved twenty-two times faster than the *trans*-isomer (106) which is, perhaps, at first sight somewhat surprising since the distance between the oxygen atoms in *cis*- and *trans*-cyclohexane-1,2-diol is the same.* However this is merely another example of the inadvisability of using preferred ground state conformation to explain reactivity.

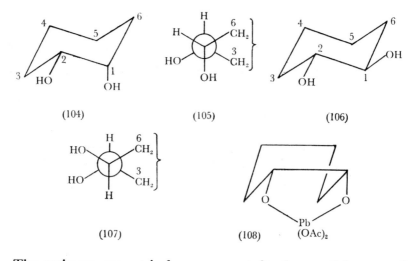

The optimum geometrical arrangement for the transition state for breakdown of the intermediate (102) has the lead atom, the two oxygen

---

* This is most readily seen by viewing along the C_1—C_2 bond giving (105) for *cis*-cyclo-hexanediol and (107) for *trans*-cyclohexanediol. Clearly the torsion angle between the C—O bonds is 60° in both cases.

atoms and the two attached carbon atoms in one plane, i.e. the two C—O bonds are syn-periplanar. This arrangement is easily achieved for *cis*-cyclohexanediol by reaction in the boat conformation, e.g., (108). However a syn-periplanar relationship of the C—O bonds of the *trans*-diol cannot be achieved in any conformation. Thus the activation energy for breakdown of the intermediate in the latter case is higher than for the *cis*-isomer.

Where the two hydroxyl groups of a *trans*-cyclohexane-1,2-diol are firmly held in a diaxial position, cleavage does not occur, except in special cases where an alternative mechanism can operate.

Cyclohexane rings, to which discussion has so far been restricted, occupy a rather special position from the conformational point of view. The chair conformation is usually so much more stable than any flexible conformations that it is preferred, even for complex polysubstituted cases. With cyclopentane, cycloheptane and their derivatives, however, no type of conformation holds pride of place and the different possible conformations often differ only slightly in energy. For this reason much less progress has been made in the conformational analysis of the other normal rings and we shall confine ourselves here to a brief summary of the situation.

Cyclopentane. The cyclopentane ring is more nearly planar than the cyclohexane ring. If, however, it were completely planar, i.e. (109), non-bonded repulsions between adjacent hydrogen atoms would be present since adjacent *cis*-C—H bonds are approximately syn-periplanar in this conformation. These interactions can be minimized by a puckering of the ring. In cyclopentane itself this puckering rotates around the ring so that no one structure can be said to be the stable conformation of cyclo-pentane. For cyclopentane derivatives, however, two puckered con-formations have been recognized which may represent energy minima in certain cases. These have been designated as the *envelope* and *half-chair* conformations.

(109)

(110)

(111)

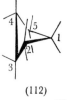

(112)

In the envelope conformation (110) four carbon atoms are in a plane and the fifth is displaced outside the plane. As indicated in (110) three hydrogens have quasi-equatorial character and three quasi-axial character in this conformation. The half-chair conformation (111) or (112)* has three carbon atoms in a plane the other two being placed one above and one below this plane. Both of these conformations involve some angle strain but this is compensated by a reduction in interactions between adjacent hydrogens. It has been suggested that in certain cyclopentane derivatives one or other of these two conformations represents the most stable conformation. Thus for a *trans*-1,2-disubstituted cyclopentane the most stable conformation is expected to be the envelope form (113) with the two substituents occupying quasi-equatorial positions. In contrast, cyclopentanone is considered to prefer the half-chair conformation (114) since this conformation possesses the minimum of non-bonded repulsions between the remaining hydrogen atoms.

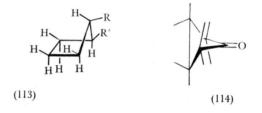

(113)   (114)

Here we have an explanation for the greater extent of dissociation of cyclopentanone cyanohydrin (Chapter 1, p. 6) as compared with cyclohexanone cyanohydrin. Cyclopentanone cyanohydrin will be destabilized relative to its ketone (114) by non-bonded repulsions between adjacent *cis*-substituents more than cyclohexanone cyanohydrin is destabilized with respect to cyclohexanone. Similarly, greater relief of strain will accompany the solvolysis of cyclopentyl tosylate (p. 6).

Cycloheptane. In cycloheptane two classes of conformations are possible, those based on a cycloheptane chair (115) and those based on a cycloheptane boat (116).

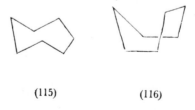

(115)   (116)

* (111) is a view of this conformation looking in the plane of the atoms $C_{(5)}$—$C_{(1)}$—$C_{(2)}$; (112) is an alternative aspect looking down on the molecule from above the $C_{(5)}$—$C_{(1)}$—$C_{(2)}$ plane.

Like the 'boat' type conformations of cyclohexane *both* these conformations are flexible and the most stable conformation of each is a twist form intermediate between two extremes. For cycloheptane itself it appears that the twist-chair conformation is of lowest energy; for substituted cycloheptanes each case needs to be considered on its merits and no satisfactory general principles can at present be propounded.

Suggestions for Further Reading (Chapter 4)

1. O. HASSEL, 'Stereochemistry of Cyclohexane', *Quarterly Reviews*, 1953, **7**, 221.
2. D. H. R. BARTON and R. C. COOKSON, 'The Principles of Conformational Analysis', *Quarterly Reviews*, 1956, **10**, 44. The above two reviews are classic expositions by pioneers in the field of conformational analysis.
3. W. G. DAUBEN and K. S. PITZER, 'Conformational Analysis', in *Steric Effects in Organic Chemistry*, ed. M. S. Newman, J. Wiley and Sons, New York, 1956, p. 1 —general review with emphasis on thermodynamic aspects.
4. W. KLYNE, 'The Conformations of Six-membered Ring Systems', in *Progress in Stereochemistry*, Butterworths, London, 1954, **1**, 36—general survey of the field.
5. H. D. ORLOFF, 'The Stereochemistry of Cyclohexane Derivatives', *Chem. Rev.*, 1954, **54**, 347—emphasises the conformational aspects of the reactions of mono- and bi-cyclic cyclohexane derivatives.
6. E. L. ELIEL, 'Conformational Analysis in Mobile Systems', *J. Chem. Educ.*, 1960, **37**, 126—monocyclic derivatives of cyclohexane and the determination of conformational free energy differences.
7. J. LEVISALLES, 'La Forme Bâteau dans les Équilibres et les Réactions des Cycles Hexatomiques', *Bull. Soc. chim. France*, 1960, 551—a timely caution concerning the dangers of neglecting flexible conformations.
8. D. H. R. BARTON and G. A. MORRISON, 'Conformational Analysis of Steroids and Related Natural Products', in *Progress in the Chemistry of Organic Natural Products*, 1961, Vol. 19, p. 165—an up-to-date survey of the conformational aspects of the reactions of polycyclic natural products.
9. E. L. ELIEL, N. L. ALLINGER, S. J. ANGYAL and G. A. MORRISON, 'Conformational Analysis', Interscience, 1965.

CHAPTER 5

BRIDGED AND CAGED RING SYSTEMS

The bridging of an alicyclic ring by one or more carbon atoms can result in a considerable restriction, or in some cases a complete removal, of conformational mobility. In the latter case, where all conformational ambiguity is removed, such rigid ring systems can serve as a testing ground for reactions which are believed to have special steric requirements. We shall deal here with only a few examples of bridged ring systems, choosing those cases where particularly interesting observations have been made. These cases should, however, serve to illustrate some of the fascinating reactions of such molecules.

Norbornane (Bicyclo[2,2,1]heptane). Bicyclo[2,2,1]heptane (1) is a completely rigid molecule of closely defined geometry, and the reactions of its derivatives have been fairly thoroughly investigated. One of the reasons for interest in this series is that many mono-terpenes, e.g., the ketone camphor (2) and the alcohol borneol (3), possess this basic skeleton. This relationship has led to the alternative and recommended name norbornane, instead of bicyclo[2,2,1]heptane.*

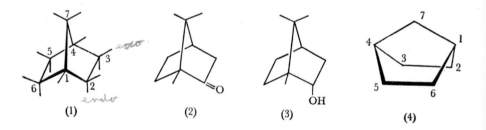

(1)   (2)   (3)   (4)

Due to the $C_{(7)}$ methylene bridge in norbornane the six-membered ring is constrained into an extreme boat conformation which is better seen in the alternative aspect of the molecule (4). There are four distinct groups of hydrogen atoms in norbornane: the two hydrogens on the methylene bridge $C_{(7)}$, the two *bridgehead* hydrogens on $C_{(1)}$ and $C_{(4)}$, the four boat-equatorial hydrogens at $C_{(2)}, C_{(3)}, C_{(5)}$ and $C_{(6)}$ (usually called *exo-hydrogens*), and the four boat-axial hydrogens on the same carbon atoms (*endo-*

---

* For nomenclature see p. 2.

hydrogens). A 2-substituted norbornane can, therefore, have either an *exo*-substituent (5) or an *endo*-substituent (6).

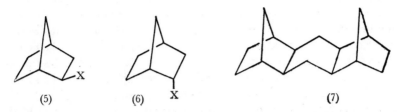

(5)   (6) X   (7)

Adjacent *exo*-substituents on $C_{(2)}$ and $C_{(3)}$ are firmly held in a syn-periplanar relationship and if two norbornane nuclei are joined through two methylene groups by their *exo*-positions the central cyclohexane ring must necessarily possess a true boat conformation (7). Suitable derivatives of (7) have been used to study the properties of substituents on boat cyclohexane rings.

Derivatives of norbornane are of particular importance in furthering our understanding of the type of carbonium ion rearrangements that occur during the complex skeletal rearrangements of terpenes. Many of the advances in this field have originated from the laboratories of S. Winstein in California.

Solvolysis Reactions of Norbornane Derivatives. One pair of compounds which are of especial significance from the point of view of carbonium ion rearrangements are the *exo-* (5, X = OBs) and *endo*-norbornyl *p*-bromo-benzenesulphonates* (6, X = OBs). We shall consider the solvolysis reactions of these substances in fair detail since, apart from their intrinsic interest, they provide a good example of the way in which mechanistic ideas evolve as additional experimental data is accumulated.

When either *exo-* or *endo*-norbornyl brosylate is acetolysed the product formed is *exo*-norbornyl acetate (5, X = OAc). However, the rate of reaction of the *exo*-brosylate, as measured by the rate of liberation of *p*-bromobenzene-sulphonic acid, is about 400 times that of the *endo*-brosylate. This fits into the picture for rearrangement reactions already described (p. 79) whereby the required stereochemistry for participation by a carbon–carbon bond is that with the migrating bond and the leaving group in an anti-periplanar relationship. Such an arrangement is only present in the *exo*-brosylate and the solvolysis of the latter is, therefore, *anchimerically* accelerated by participation of the electrons of the $C_{(1)}$—$C_{(6)}$ bond. This leads directly to an intermediate ion (8) in which the electrons of the $C_{(1)}$—$C_{(6)}$ bond have become *delocalized* as indicated: the dotted lines

* *p*-bromobenzenesulphonates, commonly called brosylates (Bs = *p*-Br.C_6H_4.SO_2^-) undergo analogous reactions to tosylates but rates are about three times faster. In other words brosylate ion is a better leaving group (anion of a stronger acid) than tosylate ion.

indicating partial bonding.* The intermediate bridged ion (8) is another example of a *non-classical* cation. It can be regarded, for some purposes, as a resonance hybrid of the two extreme classical ions (9) and (10). However, as in all cases of the use of the resonance concept, it should be remembered that the ion (8) will have properties which cannot simply be expressed by a combination of (9) and (10). In particular a classical ion such as (9) would have a 'solvation shell' of solvent molecules on both the *exo-* and *endo*-faces of the molecule, whereas the non-classical ion (8) can only be solvated from the *exo*-face. A reorganization of solvent molecules (which is difficult to represent diagrammatically) would thus be involved in a transition from ion (9) to ion (8).

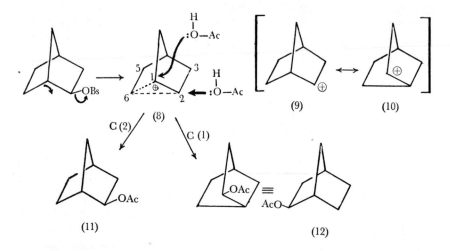

Attack of acetic acid at either of the two equivalent electron deficient centres $C_{(1)}$ or $C_{(2)}$ gives the same product 2-*exo*-norbornyl acetate (11) or (12). The two structures (11) and (12) are, of course, mirror images but this is not distinguishable where racemic starting material is used (see below). By analogy with an S_N2 reaction, attack of acetic acid should occur along a line directly opposite to the partial bonds in the non-classical ion (8) and this leads naturally to an explanation for the formation of the *exo*-norbornyl acetate and none of the *endo*-isomer.

With 2-*endo*-norbornyl brosylate the $C_{(6)}$—$C_{(1)}$ bond is not favourably placed to participate in the ionization of the brosylate ion and the alternative possibility of delocalization of the $C_{(1)}$—$C_{(7)}$ bond is sterically

---

* It is unfortunate that dotted lines now have two meanings, namely (*a*) to indicate full bonds below the plane of the paper in planar representations of cyclic molecules, and (*b*) to indicate partial bonding in non-classical ions. It should usually be clear which is being used in particular cases and the use of the two different representations together in the same formula has been avoided.

prohibited. In this case, unassisted ionization furnishes the classical ion (9); this is the rate-determining step, and is followed by electronic and solvent reorganization to give the bridged ion (8). This accounts for the slower rate of solvolysis of the *endo*-brosylate and for the observation that *exo*-norbornyl acetate is the final product of the reaction as before.

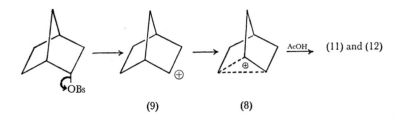

(9)   (8)

Further information about the detailed course of the reaction has been given by a study of the solvolyses of the optically active *exo*- and *endo*-norbornyl brosylates, obtained after resolution of the parent alcohols. As the intermediate bridged ion (8) is symmetrical [this is most readily seen from the alternative aspect (13)] it cannot sustain optical activity and must afford racemic *exo*-norbornyl acetate [(11) plus (12)] on reaction with acetic acid. In agreement the *exo*-norbornyl acetate obtained from the acetolysis of optically active *exo*-norbornyl brosylate is entirely racemic. That from the *endo*-brosylate is largely, but not completely, racemized and the small amount of optically active product is considered to have arisen by a direct displacement route (14).

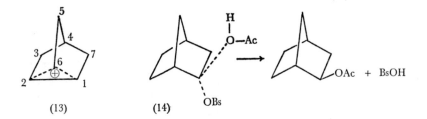

(13)   (14)

An additional point emerges from a determination of the rate of racemization of the optically active brosylates. For *endo*-norbornyl brosylate the rate of racemization is found to be the same as the rate of formation of *p*-bromobenzenesulphonic acid, after correcting for the small amount of the direct displacement reaction mentioned above. This can be accommodated by the mechanism already described if the formation of the classical ion (9) is the rate determining step for both reactions. Clearly, titratable *p*-bromobenzenesulphonic acid is being produced at a rate governed by the rate of ionization of the *endo*-brosylate; the re-organization of the classical ion (9) to the non-classical ion (8), which results in racemization, must occur in a fast subsequent step. In contrast *exo*-norbornyl brosylate is found to be racemized at a rate four times faster than the rate of liberation of *p*-bromobenzenesulphonic acid. This requires an additional refinement to the mechanism so far elaborated for the *exo*-brosylate, and has led to the proposal that the initial inter-mediate is a bridged ion-pair (15), i.e. ionization has occurred but not dissociation. The ion-pair (15) is symmetrical and hence the rate of its formation is the rate of racemization. Two alternative paths are open to this ion-pair once formed; it can undergo either (i) '*internal return*' to *racemic exo*-norbornyl brosylate by coordination of brosylate ion at $C_{(1)}$ or $C_{(2)}$, or (ii) dissociation, followed by reaction with acetic acid which will afford, as before, racemic *exo*-norbornyl acetate and *p*-bromobenzene-sulphonic acid. The rate of liberation of *p*-bromobenzenesulphonic acid corresponds to the rate of dissociation of the ion pair (15).

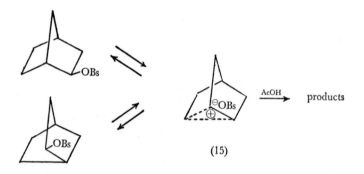

(15)

J. D. Roberts and his co-workers have obtained additional information about the mechanism of this solvolysis reaction by employing the tech-nique of ^{14}C labelling. Racemic *exo*-norbornyl brosylate equally labelled with ^{14}C at $C_{(2)}$ and $C_{(3)}$ (16) was prepared and subjected to acetolysis. On the basis of the ideas so far developed it would be expected that the *exo*-norbornyl acetate formed, would be equally labelled over carbon atoms $C_{(2)}$, $C_{(3)}$, $C_{(1)}$ and $C_{(7)}$:

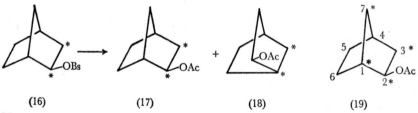

(16)   (17)   (18)   (19)

Thus 50% of the acetate formed should be labelled as in (17) and 50% as in (18); however, since the starting material was racemic this leads to a statistical labelling pattern as in (19).

When a stepwise degradation of the labelled *exo*-norbornyl acetate produced in this reaction was carried out, so as to locate the position of the labelled carbon atoms, it was found that considerable scrambling of the label had occurred. Thus ^{14}C was present at $C_{(5)}$ and $C_{(6)}$ as well as at the expected positions $C_{(1)}$ and $C_{(7)}$. A typical degradation showed 42% ^{14}C at $C_{(2)}$ and $C_{(3)}$, 42% ^{14}C at $C_{(1)}$ and $C_{(7)}$ and 15% ^{14}C at $C_{(5)}$ and $C_{(6)}$. Basically, the presence of radioactivity at $C_{(5)}$ and $C_{(6)}$ can be explained by the migration of a hydrogen atom, with its bonding electrons, from $C_{(6)}$ to $C_{(2)}$ in a classical ion,

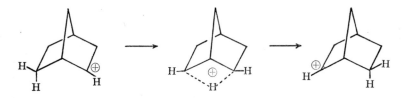

This is sometimes called a 1,3-*hydride shift*. Incorporation of this idea into the non-classical ion scheme shows that the three non-classical ions (8), (20) and (21) can be interconverted* as shown:

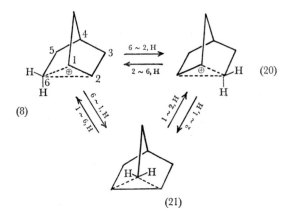

The longer the 'lifetime' of the bridged ions the greater the extent of interconversions between them; the above acetolysis results indicate that about 45% of the bridged ions formed undergo such an equilibration

* The figures above the arrows in the diagram show the hydride shifts involved. For example, 6 ∼ 2, H signifies a hydride shift from $C_{(6)}$ to $C_{(2)}$.

before reaction, while the remaining 55% react before hydride shift occurs.

When the solvolysis is carried out in formic acid, which is a poorer nucleophile than acetic acid, the distribution of ^{14}C in the resulting *exo*-norbornyl formate is compatible with almost complete equilibration of the three ions (8), (20) and (21). This agrees with the interpretation, since the cationic intermediates would be expected to have a longer life time in this solvent and hence have a greater chance of undergoing 1,3-hydride shifts.

Finally, evidence has also been accumulating which leads to the conclusion that the intermediate non-classical ions involved in the solvolysis of the norbornyl brosylates are best represented by a structure of type (22). Here the additional dotted line implies a contribution from the classical ion (23) to the non-classical structure. Perhaps the most convincing evidence for this has come from the discovery that acetolysis of 2-(cyclopent-3-enyl)ethyl *p*-nitrobenzenesulphonate (24, $X = p\text{-}NO_2C_6H_4.SO_2^-$) leads to *exo*-norbornyl acetate in over 99% yield.

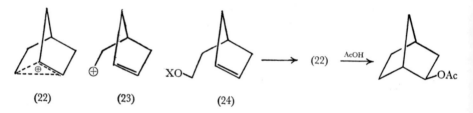

(22)   (23)   (24)

It might be objected that if the non-classical ion has the structure (22) then why is some of the acetate (24, X =Ac) not formed in the solvolysis of *exo*-norbornyl brosylate? However, since $C_{(1)}$ and $C_{(2)}$ are secondary positions while $C_{(6)}$ is primary, most of the positive charge will be borne by the first two positions. Thus in the highly exothermic reaction with acetic acid no detectable amount of the primary acetate is formed.

Several other norbornane derivatives have proved to be of considerable interest from the point of view of carbonium ion reactions and have been extensively studied. Although space is not available here to give these examples the treatment they deserve, a cursory survey should indicate the salient points of interest.

The solvolysis of *exo*-norbornenyl brosylate (25) is anchimerically accelerated and the rate is some 10,000 times that of the *endo*-isomer. [14]C labelling studies similar to those described for *exo*-norbornyl brosylate have led to the conclusion that the first formed intermediate non-classical ion, '*unsymmetrical ion*' (26), is the result of participation by the π-electrons of the double bond. Subsequent isomerization of this ion by delocalization of the electrons of the $C_{(6)}$—$C_{(1)}$ bond can give the 'symmetrical' ion (27).

The second isomerization occurs to a greater extent when solvents of low nucleophilicity are employed, since under these circumstances the first-formed ion (26) has a longer 'life-time'. Products are: nortricyclyl acetate (28) by coordination of acetic acid at $C_{(2)}$ in either cation, 'unrearranged' norbornenyl acetate from attack at $C_{(5)}$ of either cation and 'rearranged'* norbornenyl acetate from attack at $C_{(4)}$ in (27).

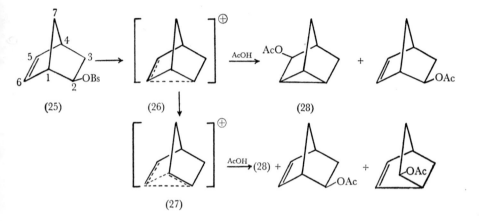

7-*Anti*norbornenyl tosylate (29) undergoes acetolysis at a rate 10^{11} times as fast as its saturated counterpart 7-norbornyl tosylate (32). The dramatic increase in rate on incorporation of the double bond into the system is explained by participation of the π-electrons of the double bond in the rate determining ionization giving the non-classical ion (30). The stereochemistry of the product (31) is that expected on the basis of the postulated non-classical intermediate which should be attacked by acetic acid from the side opposite (i.e. *anti*-) to the participating double bond. The overall result of the reaction is thus replacement of the tosylate group by acetoxyl with retention of configuration.

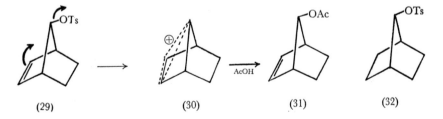

* 'Unrearranged' and 'rearranged' norbornenyl acetate can, of course, only be distinguished if the starting brosylate (25) is either optically active or labelled with ^{14}C, e.g., at $C_{(5)}$ and $C_{(6)}$.

In the epimeric *syn*-tosylate (33) the double bond cannot participate in the ionization, and participation by the electrons of the $C_{(1)}$—$C_{(6)}$ bond occurs, instead. The rate of solvolysis is some 10^4 times as fast as that of the saturated compound (32), and the product has the rearranged structure (35).*

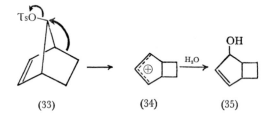

(33)   (34)   (35)

Bicyclo[2,2,2]octane. In contrast to norbornane, its ring homologue bicyclo[2,2,2]octane (36) possesses a certain degree of flexibility, as is readily apparent from Dreiding models. This means that the most stable conformation is probably somewhat 'twisted' about the axis through $C_{(1)}$ and $C_{(4)}$ to minimize the syn-periplanar interactions between adjacent hydrogen atoms on $C_{(2)}$ and $C_{(3)}$, $C_{(5)}$ and $C_{(6)}$, and $C_{(7)}$ and $C_{(8)}$. An additional distinction between norbornane and bicyclo[2,2,2]octane is that due to the high symmetry of the latter there is only one possible orientation of a 2-substituent. Thus (37) and (38) are in fact simply mirror images of one another.

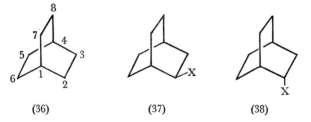

(36)   (37)   (38)

The acetolysis of bicyclo[2,2,2]oct-2-yl tosylate (39) would be expected to be anchimerically assisted by participation of the $C_{(6)}$—$C_{(1)}$ bond by analogy with *exo*-norbornyl brosylate. In the intermediate non-classical cation (40) the two important positions of partial positive charge, $C_{(1)}$ and $C_{(2)}$, are now no longer exactly equivalent as in the norbornane case. Experimentally the product of acetolysis of the tosylate (39) is found to be a mixture of 60% of the acetate (41), from co-ordination of acetic acid at $C_{(2)}$ and 40% of the acetate (42) from reaction at $C_{(1)}$.

---

* For experimental reasons the preparative reaction used was hydrolysis by aqueous sodium carbonate, thus resulting in an alcohol as product.

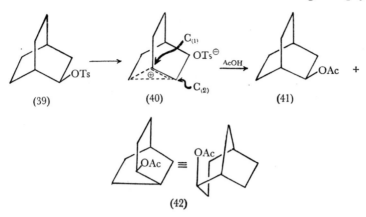

(39)   (40)   (41)

(42)

The acetate (42) is a derivative of a new bridged ring system—bicyclo[3,2,1]octane—with the acetoxyl group axially attached to the six-membered ring i.e. *cis* to the methylene bridge. That only the axial isomer of the acetate (42) is formed is good stereochemical evidence for the intermediate non-classical ion (40).

Other Bridged Ring Systems. Many other bridged ring systems are known but, on the whole, they have not been as thoroughly investigated as those already described. However, brief mention should be made of the highly strained bicyclo[2,1,1]hexane (43) system. In particular the tosylate of the alcohol (44) is interesting since it is so unstable that it rearranges on standing to 3-cyclohexenyl tosylate (45). This rearrangement probably proceeds by ion-pair intermediates as indicated.

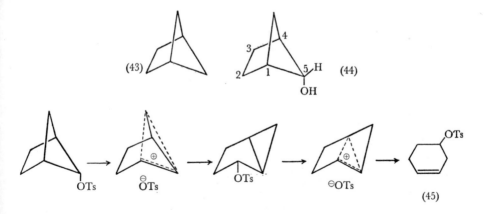

(45)

In contrast, the tosylate of the epimeric alcohol is much less reactive, presumably because participation by the $C_{(1)}$–$C_{(2)}$ bond would involve a non-classical cation much more strained than the starting material.

Two other bridged ring systems of more than routine interest are bicyclo[3,3,1]nonane and adamantane. The former might at first sight be expected to exist in the two chair conformation (46). However, in this conformation, severe non-bonded interactions between the axial hydrogen atoms at $C_{(3)}$ and $C_{(7)}$ are present. It is likely, therefore, that the preferred conformation will have one boat ring as in (47), to remove this destabilizing interaction. Interestingly the presence of the second ring holds the boat ring in a true, or classical, boat conformation. Twist-boats of the type possible in cyclohexane itself cannot occur here.

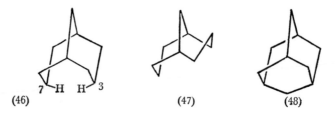

(46)   (47)   (48)

In the beautifully symmetrical molecule of the tricyclic compound adamantane (48) the two interacting axial hydrogens of the two-chair conformation of bicyclo[3,3,1]nonane are replaced by a bridging methylene group. The molecule is thus relatively rigid and all the six-membered rings are held in a chair conformation.

Bridgehead Derivatives. Bridged bicyclic molecules bearing a substituent at the bridgehead are of considerable theoretical interest from the point of view of substitution reactions. For example, the normal displacement mechanism for bimolecular nucleophilic substitution (S_N2) is not possible in 4-chlorobornane (49), due to complete shielding of the rear side of the carbon atom bearing the halogen by the cage of the ring. Furthermore, since a carbonium ion is most stable when the carbon atom bearing the positive charge is trigonal, with sp^2 hybridization, a uni-molecular ionization mechanism (S_N1) is also strongly disfavoured. This follows from the fact that, if a bridgehead carbonium ion were formed it would be forced to have a tetrahedral configuration by the geometry of the ring.

The practical consequences of the above considerations are: (*a*) that 4-chlorobornane (49) is recovered unchanged from treatment under strenuous S_N2 reaction conditions (e.g., heating with sodium ethoxide in ethanol at 205°), and (*b*) that it is only slowly hydrolysed on heating with aqueous silver nitrate at the same temperature. Typical tertiary halides are usually hydrolysed extremely rapidly by the latter reagent at much lower temperatures; in such cases the silver ion acts as an electrophilic catalyst for ionization:

$$R_3C\text{—}Cl\ldots\ldots Ag^\oplus \longrightarrow R_3C^\oplus + AgCl$$

An interesting corollary of the difficulty of forming a bridgehead carbonium ion is that the tosylate (50) can be prepared from the corresponding alcohol in the usual way. This possesses the distinction of being the only known tertiary tosylate. As a rule attempts to prepare the tosylate of a tertiary alcohol lead only to the products expected from decomposition *via* the carbonium ion.

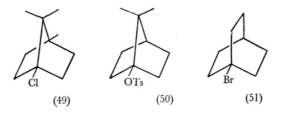

(49)   (50)   (51)

With increasing ring size, bridgehead carbonium ions become more readily accessible due to the greater flexibility of the system, e.g., the first order rate constant for S_N1 type hydrolysis of 1-bromobicyclo[2,2,2]-octane (51) in 70% aqueous dioxane at 100° is 0.68×10^{-6}. This may be compared with the value of 0.82 for t-butyl bromide under similar conditions.

Another example of the effect of ring size on the ease of formation of bridgehead carbonium ions is given by the course of the reaction of the two bridgehead alcohols (52) and (53) with thionyl chloride. The nor-bornane derivative (52) reacts to give a stable chlorosulphite (54) while the bicyclo[3,2,2]nonane yields the chloride (55) together with sulphur dioxide. This is regarded as evidence that the usual course of decomposition of a chlorosulphite to an alkyl chloride involves ionization to an ion-pair which subsequently collapses to alkyl chloride and sulphur dioxide:

$$R_3C\!-\!OH \xrightarrow{\ SOCl_2\ } R_3C\!-\!O\!-\!\overset{\overset{O}{\|}}{S}\!-\!Cl \longrightarrow R_3C^{\oplus} \ \underset{O}{\overset{O}{\diagdown}}\!S\!-\!Cl \longrightarrow R_3C\!-\!Cl + SO_2$$

In the norbornane case the chlorosulphite (54) is stable because ionization would produce a strongly unfavoured bridgehead carbonium ion. This restriction does not apply to the more flexible bicyclo[3,2,2]nonane system (53).

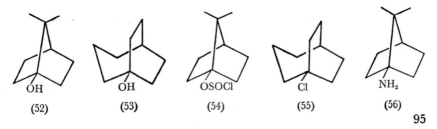

(52)   (53)   (54)   (55)   (56)

95

The only bridgehead carbonium ion reaction of the smaller bicyclic systems which proceeds satisfactorily is the deamination of bridgehead amines with nitrous acid. For example, the amine (56) can be converted into the alcohol (52) in this way. In this reaction the intermediate diazonium ion is so unstable, due to the great driving force associated with cleavage to the highly stable nitrogen molecule, that even energetically unfavoured bridgehead carbonium ions can be obtained:

$$\overset{|}{\underset{|}{C}}-NH_2 \xrightarrow{HNO_2} \overset{|}{\underset{|}{C}}-\overset{\oplus}{N}\equiv N \longrightarrow N_2 + \overset{|}{\underset{|}{C}}{}^{\oplus} \xrightarrow{H_2O} \overset{|}{\underset{|}{C}}-OH$$

In contrast to the difficulty of formation of a carbonium ion at the bridgehead of a bicyclic bridged molecule the corresponding anion and radical appear to be relatively accessible. There would, therefore, seem to be less destabilization associated with a tetrahedral carbanion or carbon radical than with a tetrahedral carbonium ion. An example of a reaction which effectively involves a bridgehead anion is the metallation of 4-chlorobornane (57) using lithium, which takes place without difficulty. The lithium derivative so formed undergoes the usual carboxylation reaction with carbon dioxide to give the bridgehead acid (58).

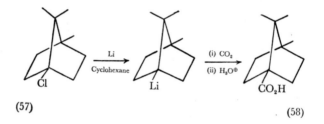

(57)   (58)

An interesting case of a reaction which proceeds by way of a bridge-head radical is provided by the radical-chain decarbonylation of the bridgehead aldehyde (59) catalysed by t-butylperoxide (See page 97).

Bredt's Rule. Another significant consequence of the rigid geometry of bicyclic bridged molecules was recognized by the German chemist Bredt in the heroic days of terpene chemistry. He realized that a molecule such as (60), with a double bond at the bridgehead, is sterically impossible and is incapable of existence. This becomes abundantly clear if one attempts to construct a model of such a molecule from ball and spring models, which usually permit the construction of models of even highly strained molecules. It should, however, be clear even without the aid of models, that the demands of a double bond, which require that the four atoms attached to the carbon atoms of the double bond be in one plane, cannot be met at the bridgehead. This rule applies only to those bicyclic

96

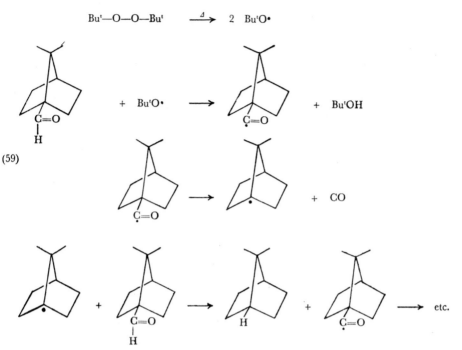

(59)

molecules which have at least one atom in each of the three bridges. Thus there are no restrictions applying to $\Delta^{1,9}$-octalin(bicyclo[4,4,0]dec-1-ene) (61) which can be prepared without difficulty.

Bredt's rule does not apply to bridged ring systems involving large rings, an aspect which will be dealt with in Chapter 6.

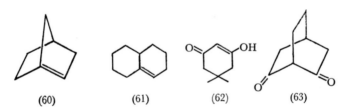

(60)   (61)   (62)   (63)

An obvious application of Bredt's rule is in structure elucidation, since it excludes from consideration those structures for an unknown compound which possess a double bond at a bridgehead. Thus in a norbornane derivative there are only two possible positions for a double bond, i.e., either between $C_{(2)}$ and $C_{(3)}$ or between $C_{(5)}$ and $C_{(6)}$.

Other, more subtle consequences of Bredt's rule may influence the structure and reactions of bridged ring compounds. Two typical examples will be considered here.

97

A normal cyclic or acyclic β-diketone is usually almost completely enolized, e.g., dimedone in water exists to about 96% in the form of the enol (62). In contrast the β-diketone (63) from bicyclo[2,2,2]octane cannot enolize in this way, since this would involve a double bond at a bridgehead, and it exhibits none of the properties of enolic compounds.

A more dramatic result of Bredt's rule is provided by the observation that the β-ketoacid (64) (ketopinic acid) is a stable compound and does not decarboxylate on heating. In contrast, a 'normal' β-keto-acid, e.g., acetoacetic acid (65), readily decarboxylates on gentle heating. The different behaviour of these two acids is additional evidence that the decarboxylation of a β-keto-acid involves formation of the enol form of the ketone as intermediate, e.g., the enol form of acetone (66). Such an enol cannot be formed in the case of the acid (64) as the double bond would be at the bridgehead.

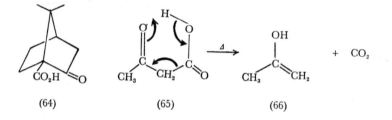

(64)   (65)   (66)

Suggestions for Further Reading (Chapter 5)

1. S. WINSTEIN, 'Some Recent Aspects of Carbonium Ion Behaviour', *Experientia Supplementum* II, p. 137—a summary and further references on carbonium ion reactions with emphasis on bridged rings.
2. U. SCHÖLLKOPF, 'Substitution Reactions at the Bridgehead of Bicyclic Compounds', *Angewandte Chemie*, 1960, **72**, 147.
3. F. S. FAWCETT, 'Bredt's Rule', *Chem. Reviews*, 1950, **47**, 219.

CHAPTER 6

MEDIUM AND LARGE RINGS

In considering the thermochemical stabilities of the cycloalkanes (Chapter 1) we saw that those with eight to eleven members inclusive—the medium ring cycloalkanes—had a relatively higher enthalpy than cyclohexane. This was taken as evidence for strain of some sort in these hydrocarbons, and to distinguish it from the classical angle strain associated with small ring compounds it was termed 'non-classical' strain. Since, as we shall see, medium ring compounds undergo a variety of interesting reactions directly or indirectly attributable to non-classical strain, it will be with these compounds that most of this chapter is concerned. In general the large ring compounds with twelve or more members differ little in their reactions from their aliphatic counterparts.

Non-classical Strain and the Conformation of Medium Rings.
We are now in a position to consider the origin of non-classical strain in medium rings. In principle it could be due to one or more of three structural causes: (i) deformation of the $C\!\!-\!\!\overset{\frown}{C}\!\!-\!\!C$ valency angle, i.e. compression *or* expansion from the preferred tetrahedral value (Baeyer type strain), (ii) partial butane interactions of the syn-periplanar or anti-clinal type (Pitzer strain, see p. 51), (iii) non-bonded interactions between hydrogen atoms *across* the ring (transannular interactions). Due to the considerable flexibility of medium rings, readily apparent on inspection of the Dreiding model of, e.g., cyclodecane, the prediction of the preferred conformation of a medium ring compound is extremely difficult. For this reason recourse has been taken to the X-ray determination of structures to give a less ambiguous result. In this way the conformations of derivatives of cyclononane and cyclodecane have been determined in the solid state, and a reasonable case has been made that these conformations are approximately preserved in the liquid state and in solution. V. Prelog and his co-workers at Zürich have been most active in this field.

To illustrate the problem of the conformational analysis of medium rings we shall confine ourselves here largely to the case of cyclodecane where the conformation is more readily represented in two dimensions. The preferred conformation of cyclodecane, as determined by an X-ray analysis of the structure of *trans*-1,6-diaminocyclodecane dihydrochloride, is shown in (1). The schematic derivation of this conformation

99

from two chair cyclohexane rings joined by 1,3-axial bonds is indicated in (2).

Closer examination of this conformational model for cyclodecane reveals that there are two anti-parallel partial butane conformations, i.e., $[C_{(9)}, C_{(10)}, C_{(1)} \text{ and } C_{(2)}]$ and $[C_{(4)}, C_{(5)}, C_{(6)} \text{ and } C_{(7)}]$, and that the remaining eight partial butane conformations are syn-clinal. This corresponds to little strain in the Pitzer sense. The detailed X-ray analysis shows, however, that some of the C—Ĉ—C angles in cyclodecane are considerably greater than the tetrahedral angle, i.e., angle strain is present. In addition the two sets of hydrogen atoms joined by dotted lines in (1) are only about 1·8 Å apart, indicating considerable transannular non-bonded repulsions. We may conclude that non-classical strain in cyclodecane

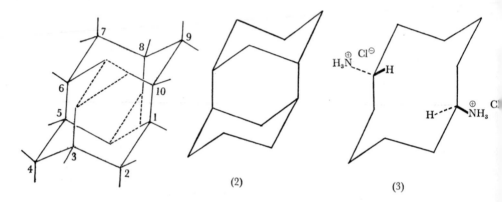

(2)   (3)

results from a combination of angle strain and transannular interactions between hydrogen atoms, though the relative importance of these factors is not easy to assess.

Broadly speaking, similar conclusions apply to cyclononane though it appears that angle strain, due to increased C—Ĉ—C angles, is more important in this instance.

Derivatives of Cyclodecane. The hydrogen atoms of cyclodecane may be divided into two main classes: (i) the six which are subject to trans-annular repulsions; these may be termed *intra-annular* hydrogens, and (ii) the remaining fourteen, called *extra-annular* hydrogens, which are not subject to any strong steric interactions. It is thus to be expected that the preferred conformation for a mono-substituted cyclodecane will be one with the substituent in an extra-annular position. In a polysubstituted cyclodecane that conformation with the maximum number of extra-annular substituents will be favoured. In agreement, the conformation of *trans*-1,6-diaminocyclodecane dihydrochloride is as in (3).

Cyclodecanone, with one trigonal atom in the ring, is expected to exist in its preferred conformation with the carbonyl group at $C_{(1)}$, $C_{(5)}$, $C_{(6)}$ or $C_{(10)}$ in (1). In this way two of the transannular interactions between hydrogen atoms present in cyclodecane will have been relieved.

Strain and the Stability of Unsaturated Medium Rings. With the increasingly flexible medium rings and large rings the introduction of such sterically demanding units as *trans*-double bonds and triple bonds becomes possible. For example, both *cis*-cyclodecene (5) and *trans*-cyclodecene (6)* are known compounds. This is in contrast with cyclohexene (4) in which only a *cis*-double bond can be accommodated.

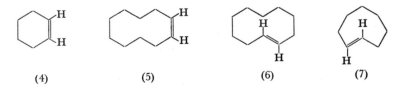

(4)   (5)   (6)   (7)

The interesting question is: What is the smallest possible ring that can contain a *trans*-double bond? This is not an easy question to answer; one approach is to try and apply to medium rings a synthetic method that is known to succeed with large rings. In this way one defines not the smallest ring which can exist containing a *trans*-double bond but the smallest ring containing a *trans*-double bond which can be prepared by a given method. So far *trans*-cyclo-octene is the smallest ring known containing a *trans*-double bond. As ring size is increased from eight onwards the stability of the *trans*- with respect to the *cis*-cyclo-olefin steadily increases. Equilibrium between *cis*- (8) and *trans*-cycloalkenes (9) can be established by heating in acetic acid containing a trace of *p*-toluenesulphonic acid. The following values have been obtained for the equilibrium constants for the conversion of *trans*- to *cis*-olefin at 100°: cyclononene, 232; cyclodecene, 12·2; cycloundecene, 0·41; cyclododecene, 0·52. Clearly the usual stability order holds true for the larger rings.

$$(\overbrace{CH_2)_{n-2}}\begin{array}{c}-CH \\ \| \\ -CH\end{array} \quad \underset{-H^{\oplus}}{\overset{+H^{\oplus}}{\rightleftharpoons}} \quad (\overbrace{CH_2)_{n-2}}\begin{array}{c}-CH_2 \\ | \\ -CH^{\oplus}\end{array} \quad \underset{+H^{\oplus}}{\overset{-H^{\oplus}}{\rightleftharpoons}} \quad (\overbrace{CH_2)_{n-2}}\begin{array}{c}-C^{H} \\ | \\ H^{C}-\end{array}$$

(8)   (9)

Another sterically demanding grouping of interest in this connection is the triple bond, which requires that for maximum stability the four carbon atoms $C-C{\equiv}C-C$ be linear. In fact the smallest stable cycloalkyne

* Planar representations are used here since not sufficient is known about the preferred conformations.

101

which has been prepared is cyclo-octyne (10) obtained by mercuric oxide oxidation of cyclo-octane-1,2-dione dihydrazone.

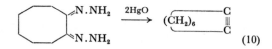

There is some evidence that cycloheptyne, cyclohexyne and even cyclopentyne may have a transitory existence as reactive intermediates. Thus treatment of cycloheptane-1,2-dione dihydrazone (11) with mercuric oxide in the presence of the very reactive Diels-Alder diene (12) yields an adduct (13) which is probably formed by Diels-Alder addition to cycloheptyne. The adduct is obtained in 35% yield. Similar experiments in the six- and five-membered ring series have given adducts corresponding to (13) in yields of 25 and 0·5% respectively. It is not to be expected that such highly strained compounds as the normal ring cyclo-alkynes can be isolated. The best that can be hoped for is indirect evidence of the above nature in which the highly reactive product is 'trapped' by reaction with a suitable substrate.

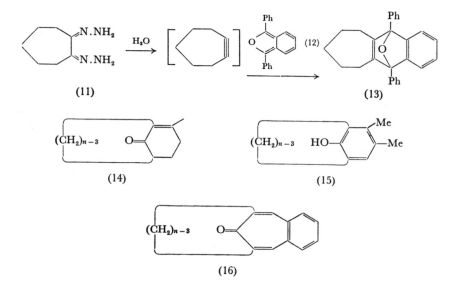

It is convenient to consider here those exceptions to Bredt's rule (p. 96) that involve large rings. Clearly the incorporation of bridgehead double bonds into bridged bicyclic molecules becomes possible if the component rings are large enough. The chief point of interest is the critical ring size below which bridgehead double bonds are not possible.

102

Again the best that can be done is to find out experimentally the smallest ring size for which a particular synthetic procedure will succeed.

A number of molecules have been synthesized which are formal exceptions to Bredt's rule. It appears that if one ring is six-membered or aromatic, the minimum size for the bridging ring is eight-membered. Thus in the series (14) and (15) the smallest ring synthesized had $n = 8$. In another series (16), where the ring being bridged is seven membered the limit was reached at $n = 7$.

REACTIONS OF MEDIUM RING COMPOUNDS

Having discussed some of the structural and conformational aspects of medium ring compounds we can now proceed to a consideration of their reactions. Of particular interest are those reactions where non-classical strain leads to qualitative or quantitative differences in comparison with the reactions of normal rings.

We briefly encountered one example each of an equilibrium controlled and a kinetically controlled reaction in medium rings in Chapter 1, and we are now in a position to discuss these in somewhat greater detail.

With regard to the dissociation constants of cyanohydrins (p. 6) it should now be clear from the above discussion that non-classical strain in a medium ring compound comprised of tetrahedral ring members is due partly to expanded $C\!-\!\overset{\frown}{C}\!-\!C$ valency angles and partly to transannular interactions between substituents. Both of these strain factors will be partially relieved in conversion of a tetrahedral cyanohydrin into the trigonal ketone. Consequently medium ring cyanohydrins are expected to have larger dissociation constants than those of normal ring ketones; this is in agreement with observation.

For solvolysis of cycloalkyl tosylates (p. 6), which is a rate controlled reaction, non-classical strain is expected to lead to relatively high rates of solvolysis due to release of strain in the transition state. The rate differences found clearly vindicate these ideas.

In contrast to the dramatic influence of ring size on those reactions in which change in coordination occurs at a ring member, other reactions, e.g., the rates of saponification of the acetates of cyclic alcohols (17), are

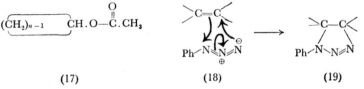

(17)   (18)   (19)

but little affected by a variation in ring size. In the latter case reaction involves attack of hydroxide ion on the carbonyl carbon atom of the acetate and this would not be expected to be affected by a variation in ring size.

One reaction of olefins which is considered to be diagnostic of strained double bonds is of interest, namely addition of phenyl azide. The reaction, which gives a triazine (19), may be considered as a direct addition as in (18) and the ease, or rate of reaction is greater the more strained the olefin. Thus *trans*-cyclo-octene which, as already discussed, is expected to be highly strained, reacts readily with phenyl azide in the above fashion while its *cis*-isomer (strain free) only reacts extremely slowly.

Other reactions of medium ring compounds, which merit discussion in rather greater detail are (*a*) elimination reactions, and (*b*) reactions involving atoms across the ring—the so-called transannular reactions.

(*a*) **Elimination Reactions in Medium Rings.** We have seen that where the two geometrical isomers of a cyclic olefin are obtainable the *cis*-isomer is more stable in eight-, nine- and ten-membered rings. It is thus at first sight surprising that the kinetically controlled product of a number of elimination reactions in medium ring compounds is the *trans*-olefin. Thus application of the Hofmann elimination (cf. p. 70) to cyclononyl- (20, $n = 9$) and cyclodecyl trimethylammonium hydroxide (20, $n = 10$) gives almost pure *trans*-cycloalkene along with very little *cis*-cycloalkene. Even with cyclo-octyltrimethylammonium hydroxide (20, $n = 8$) a mixture of *trans*- and *cis*-cyclo-octene in the proportions 3:2 results, although *trans*-cyclo-octene is thermodynamically much less stable than the *cis*-isomer. Apparently the energy of activation for anti-coplanar elimination *via* the partial conformation (21) is lower than that for elimination by way of (22) for a medium ring compound. Conformation (21) would lead to a *trans*-cyclo-olefin and (22) to a *cis*-cyclo-olefin.

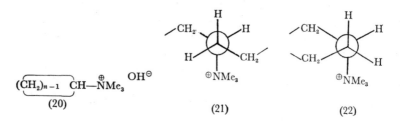

In the case of the ten-membered ring this can be understood in terms of the conformation (1) already developed for cyclodecane. This leads to the preferred conformation (23) for elimination in cyclodecyltrimethyl ammonium hydroxide. Here the larger substituent occupies an extra-annular position and the partial conformation $C_{(10)}$, $C_{(1)}$, $C_{(2)}$ and $C_{(3)}$ is that depicted in (21). Anti-coplanar elimination leads directly to *trans*-cyclo-decene (24). An additional factor favouring elimination *via* conformation (23) is that, in forming the transition state for elimination, transannular interactions associated with the intra-annular hydrogens on $C_{(1)}$ and $C_{(2)}$ are relieved.

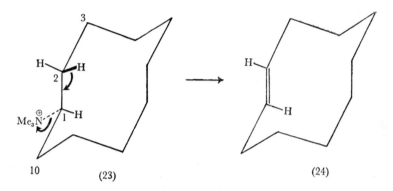

Similar considerations must also explain the preference for formation of *trans*-isomers in the other rings, but an explicit rationalization cannot be so readily made.

It is of interest that *cis*-elimination reactions also lead to predominant formation of *trans*-cycloalkenes in medium ring compounds. An example of such a reaction is the pyrolysis of amine oxides where a *cis*-relationship between the proton being eliminated and the amine oxide group is required. The basis for this geometrical requirement is that a five-membered cyclic transition state (25) is involved.

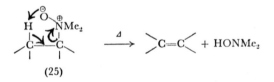

In conformation (26) for cyclodecyldimethylamine oxide only slight distortion of the molecule is required to bring the $C_{(1)}$—N bond into a synperiplanar relationship with the *cis*-$C_{(2)}$—H bond. *cis*-Elimination can then occur to give the *trans*-olefin (24), cf. partial conformations (27), (28) and (29). Again strain due to transannular interactions is partially relieved in the transition state.

(*b*) **Transannular Reactions.** One of the characteristic structural features of medium ring compounds is the close proximity of the intra-annular hydrogen atoms to the carbon atoms across the ring. This raises the possibility that if a positive charge be generated on a ring carbon atom of a medium ring then migration of a hydrogen atom, with its bonding electrons, might occur across the ring to give an isomeric ion.

We can examine the situation more closely in terms of the conformational model (1) for cyclodecane. In solvolysis of cyclodecyl tosylate, for example, it is expected that ionization will occur in, e.g., conformation (30), where the tosyloxy grouping occupies an extra-annular position. Only in such a conformation can relief of transannular interactions*

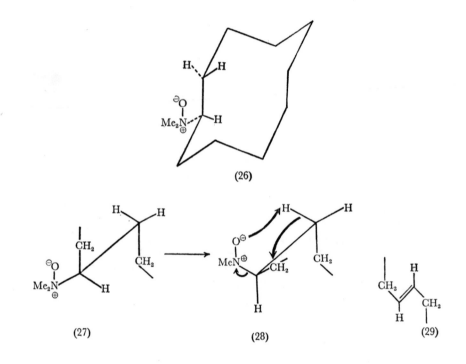

(26)

(27)   (28)   (29)

accompany ionization. The resulting carbonium ion (31) can then undergo either the normal reactions of a carbonium ion, e.g., elimination of an α-proton or reaction with solvent, or the above-mentioned isomerization by transannular migration of hydrogen. In the carbonium ion (31) where the lobes of the vacant p-orbital are indicated, the closest intra-annular hydrogen atoms are those on $C_{(5)}$ and $C_{(6)}$. Migration of either of these hydrogen atoms, with their bonding electrons, gives respectively the ions (32) and (33). Ion (32) is said to have been formed by a 1,5-hydride shift and (33) by a 1,6-hydride shift.

* i.e., interactions between the hydrogen on $C_{(1)}$ and the intra-annular hydrogens on $C_{(5)}$ and $C_{(8)}$.

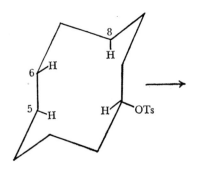

(30)

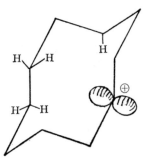

(31)

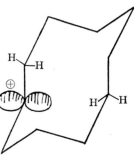

(32)

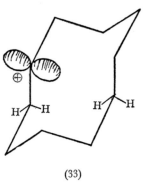

(33)

Such 1,5- and 1,6-hydride shifts may be compared with the 1,2-hydride shifts which occur in isomerization of secondary to tertiary carbonium ions, e.g., (34)→(35), and the 1,3-hydride shifts which occur in norbornane derivatives (36)→(37) (see p. 89).

$$CH_3{\scriptstyle\diagdown}\!\underset{\underset{H}{|}}{C}\!\!-\!\overset{\oplus}{C}H\!\!-\!CH_3 \longrightarrow CH_3\!\!-\!\underset{\underset{H}{\oplus}}{\overset{CH_3}{|}}\!\!-\!CH\!\!-\!CH_3 \longrightarrow CH_3\!\!-\!\underset{\oplus}{\overset{CH_3}{|}}\!\!-\!CH_2\!\!-\!CH_3$$

(34)   (35)

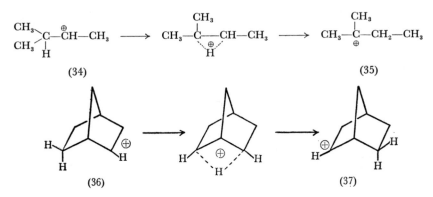

(36)   (37)

The incursion of transannular hydride shifts is, of course, not directly observable in cyclodecyl tosylate itself, since carbonium ions (31), (32) and (33) are in fact identical. If, however, one of the carbon atoms is

107

uniquely identifiable, either by ¹⁴C labelling or by substitution of hydrogen by deuterium, then an experimental demonstration of transannular hydride migration becomes possible. In fact both types of labelling experiment have been carried out and they show that transannular hydride migration occurs to a substantial extent. We shall describe here only the deuterium labelling experiment since the results are more readily presented in this case.

Acetolysis of the tosylate of cyclodecanol (38) labelled with deuterium at $C_{(1)}$ gave, as main product, a mixture of cyclodecenes in which the *trans*-isomer predominates. If the reaction had proceeded in a 'classical' fashion all the deuterium in the product should lie at the vinyl positions $C_{(1)}$ and $C_{(2)}$ (40). Oxidative cleavage of (40) should, therefore, give sebacic acid (41) free from deuterium. In fact it was found that the sebacic acid contained 16% of the deuterium present in the starting tosylate. Further stepwise degradation of the sebacic acid showed that virtually all the residual deuterium was attached to $C_{(5)}$, $C_{(6)}$, $C_{(7)}$ and $C_{(8)}$. This result can be readily accommodated if concurrent 1,5- and 1,6-hydride shifts occur in 16% of the carbonium ions (39) before elimination; i.e. (42) → (43), (44) and (45).* Remembering that cyclodecene has a plane of symmetry through the double bond the required labelling of $C_{(5)}$, $C_{(6)}$, $C_{(7)}$ and $C_{(8)}$ is obtained.

It is clearly possible to have carbonium ion reactions in suitably substituted medium ring compounds where the products derived by a

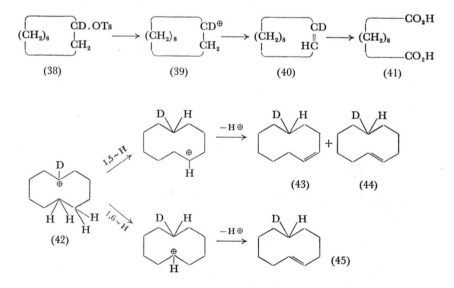

(38)   (39)   (40)   (41)

(42)   (43)   (44)   (45)

---

* For simplicity planar formulae are used here without any stereochemical implications.

108

'classical' route and those obtained by way of a transannular hydride shift are different compounds. In fact it was with such reactions that transannular hydride shifts were first discovered.

Typical of such reactions is the acid catalysed opening of epoxides derived from medium ring cycloalkenes. As we have already seen in Chapter 4 (p. 73) the expected product from the acid catalysed cleavage of a normal ring epoxide is the *trans*-1,2-diol or, where the acid used is formic acid, the monoformate of a *trans*-1,2-diol, i.e. (46) → (47).

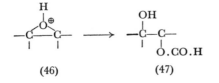

(46)   (47)

When a medium ring epoxide, e.g., *cis*-cyclo-octene epoxide (48), is heated in formic acid and the intermediate product hydrolysed to the free alcohols the resulting mixture contains, in addition to the 'classical' product [*trans*-1,2-cyclo-octanediol (49)] *cis*-1,4-cyclo-octanediol (50), cyclo-oct-3-enol (51) and cyclo-oct-4-enol (52).

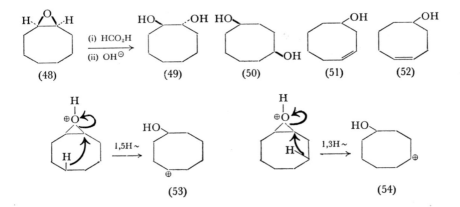

(48)   (49)   (50)   (51)   (52)

(53)   (54)

The gross structures of the abnormal products (50–52) can be explained by either a 1,5- or a 1,3-hydride shift. This is readily seen if we write down the classical ions (53) and (54) which would result from such shifts. These ions are, of course, identical; coordination with solvent would give the monoformate of cyclo-octane-1,4-diol while elimination of a proton from the two alternative positions leads to the unsaturated alcohols (51) and (52). Clearly something more than purely conformational factors is involved since, if a classical ion such as (53) were a true intermediate it should react with solvent with equal probability from either side to give a mixture of the *cis*- and *trans*-1,4-diols. The fact that only the *cis*-isomer is formed suggests that bridged 'non-classical' ions are involved. Although we can at present only guess at the required conformation, the reaction can be discussed in terms of structures (55) and (58). Conformation (55) can lead to the bridged ion (56) by 1,5-hydride shift. Clearly the bridging hydrogen 'shields' the upper face of the molecule so that attack of formic acid occurs from beneath, (*cis* to the original epoxide ring) giving (57). Similarly for a 1,3-hydride shift we have (58) → (59) → (60).

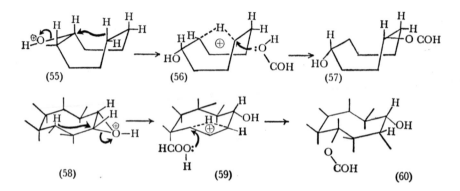

The proportion of *cis*-1,4-cyclo-octanediol formed by the two routes has been determined using epoxide labelled with deuterium at $C_{(5)}$ and $C_{(6)}$. Only a 1,5-hydride shift can lead to deuterium migration; analysis of the product on this basis has shown that 61% of the *cis*-1,4-cyclo-octanediol is formed by a 1,5-hydride shift and 39% by a 1,3-hydride shift.

Formolysis of *trans*-cyclo-octene epoxide gives *trans*-1,4-cyclo-octane-diol monoformate as major product in an analogous fashion. Again a non-classical ion can be invoked to account for the stereospecificity of the reaction and the reaction may be represented in terms of the conformation (61) for *trans*-cyclo-octene epoxide.

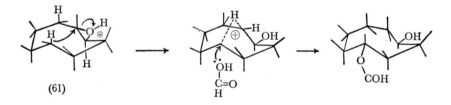

The formation of 'abnormal' diols by a transannular route has been shown to be a general reaction for epoxides from medium ring cyclo-alkenes. Detailed discussion of these further examples will not be attempted here.

Transannular Cyclization Reactions. Due to the proximity of atoms across a medium ring, reactions can occur in which a transannular bond is formed, often concomitantly with transannular hydride shifts in carbonium ion reactions. For example, in the formolysis of *trans*-cyclodecene oxide (62) where the product of transannular hydride shift is the monoformate of the 1,6-glycol (63) an accompanying product is a 1-decalol (64). Clearly the latter has been obtained by elimination of a proton across the ring with formation of a transannular bond.* Thus the glycol monoformate (63) has been formed by a 1,5-transannular hydride shift while the decalol (64) is the result of a 1,6-transannular elimination of a proton.

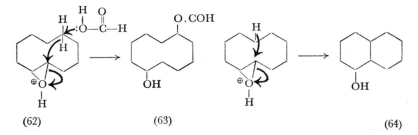

A reaction which leads solely to transannular cyclization occurs when the tosylate of 6-hydroxycyclodecanone (65) is heated in ethanol in the presence of catalytic quantities of acid. The product, the bicyclic ketone (66), is formed by transannular participation by the double bond of the enol in the ionization of tosylate ion.

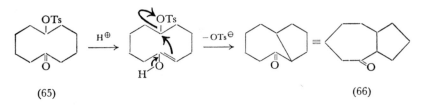

Another example of a transannular cyclization involves the intramolecular reaction of medium ring carbenes. The appropriate carbenes are produced by decomposition of diazocycloalkanes in an aprotic solvent (see p. 24), for example see top of next page.

Finally an interesting group of transannular cyclizations are known which are effectively intramolecular Diels-Alder reactions. The first example of this kind was the conversion of either cyclo-octa-1,3,5-triene (67) or bicyclo[4,2,0]octa-2,4-diene (68) into an equilibrium mixture of

---

* Planar formulae have been used to represent the transformations as there is some doubt as to the precise stereochemistry of the products.

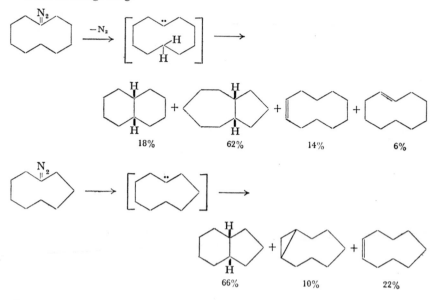

the two on heating. Here we have an example of two isomers, differing only in their bonding, being readily interconverted. The phenomenon is sometimes known as valency-bond tautomerism.

Two important factors controlling such reactions are, (i) the free energy of activation of the process, i.e. the height of the free energy barrier between the two isomers, and (ii) the relative thermodynamic stability of the two isomers. The first factor determines whether or not the two separate isomers can be isolated as discrete entities and the second governs the composition of the equilibrium mixture. In the case of cyclo-octatriene (67) the energy barrier is such that the two individual isomers (67) and (68) can be isolated separately in the pure form at room temperature. On heating, the energy barrier is surmounted and, at equilibrium, the mixture contains 85% of the triene and 15% of the bicyclic olefin (68).

For cycloheptatriene* (69) it appears, firstly that the energy barrier between it and its possible valency bond tautomer norcaradiene (70) is so low that interconversion occurs at room temperature, and secondly that the 'equilibrium mixture' contains no detectable amount of nor-caradiene. Thus all attempts to synthesize norcaradiene have given only

* Sometimes called tropilidene.

cycloheptatriene. Seemingly the angle strain in (70) destabilizes it with respect to the monocyclic isomer. In the case of cyclo-octatriene (67) angle strain in (68) is roughly balanced by the non-classical strain in (67).

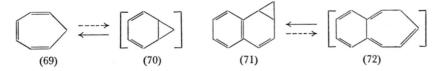

(69)   (70)   (71)   (72)

With the benzonorcaradiene (71) it again appears that the energy barrier between (71) and (72) is too low to allow of their separate isolation. This time, however, the position of equilibrium favours the norcaradiene isomer, presumably due to the intact benzene ring present in (71).

Introduction of substituents onto such valency-bond tautomeric systems may completely alter the energy situation. Thus with two additional methoxycarbonyl groups, i.e. (73)→(74), the cyclo-octatriene system is tipped completely in favour of the monocyclic form presumably by stabilization due to conjugation.

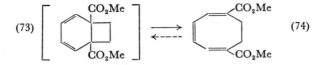

(73)   (74)

Other relevant examples of valency bond tautomerism involving medium rings are summarized below; they show an interesting balance between angle strain and non-classical strain. Where one member of the pair is not isolable it is placed in square brackets.

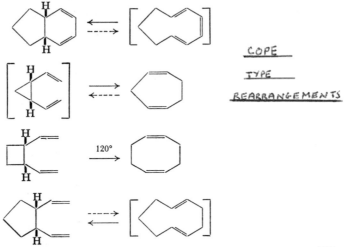

COPE TYPE REARRANGEMENTS

113

Medium and Large Ring Conjugated Cyclopolyolefins. Even-membered rings containing a closed chain of conjugated double bonds are of interest in connection with Hückel's $(4n+2)$ π-electron rule (p. 43), which predicts that only the systems with 2, 6, 10, etc. electrons will possess 'aromatic' character.

Cyclo-octatetraene. Perhaps the most interesting compound of this type is cyclo-octatetraene (75) which strikingly confirms the predictions of Hückel's rule in having very different properties from those of benzene. It possesses a puckered 'tub' conformation (76) in which efficient conjugation between the double bonds is sterically prohibited in the ground state.

(75)   (76)

Cyclo-octatetraene was originally synthesized in 1911 by Willstätter in a classical degradation of the alkaloid pseudopelletierine. Although doubt was cast on this synthesis for many years afterwards, it was finally vindicated by a modern repetition. In addition, the properties ascribed by Willstätter to his cyclo-octatetraene were in complete agreement with those for cyclo-octatetraene now produced from acetylene by action of nickel cyanide in tetrahydrofuran. This latter synthesis, which was one of several incredible reactions discovered by the German chemist W. Reppe during the war years, is believed to proceed by way of an octahedral complex of four molecules of acetylene with nickel cyanide.

The chemical properties of cyclo-octatetraene are those of an unsaturated highly reactive compound, quite different from those of benzene. Many of the reactions of cyclo-octatetraene lead to products in which rearrangement of the skeleton has occurred. In particular, in one group of reactions cyclo-octatetraene appears to be reacting as if it had the valency tautomeric structure (77); e.g., bromination gives the dibromide (78) and a Diels-Alder reaction with maleic anhydride affords the adduct (79). Since, however, the structure of cyclo-octatetraene is firmly established, ring bridging must be occurring during these reactions.

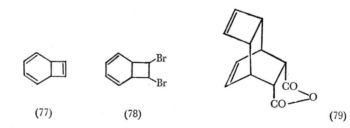

(77)   (78)   (79)

Probably the most revealing of all the interesting reactions undergone by cyclo-octatetraene, at least from the point of view of aromaticity, is its reduction by potassium in tetrahydrofuran to a dipotassium salt. All available evidence indicates that the latter has a planar structure, (80) possessing a ten π-electron system, analogous in many ways to the cyclopentadienyl anion.

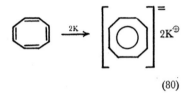

(80)

Higher Cyclopolyolefins. Other conjugated cyclopolyolefins are obviously of interest in connection with theories of aromaticity. However, in order to achieve a completely conjugated system (i.e. efficient π-overlap) it is necessary that such molecules should be planar, or nearly so. For example, in the unknown compound cyclododecahexaene (81), if the molecule were planar the three hydrogen atoms which are directed towards the centre of the molecule would interfere strongly, thereby introducing a considerable destabilizing factor. However, cyclo-octadecanonaene (82) might be expected to be fairly free from such destabilizing interactions. This interesting compound has been prepared starting from the diacetylene hexa-1,5-diyne (84). Oxidative coupling of the latter in the presence of cupric acetate gave the cyclic trimer (85) and prototropic rearrangement of (85) formed the conjugated hexa-ene-triyne (86). Finally partial hydrogenation of (86) over Lindlar catalyst gave the cyclopolyolefin (82). It forms brownish red crystals which can be sublimed at 120°/0·5 mm. and only slowly decomposes on exposure to

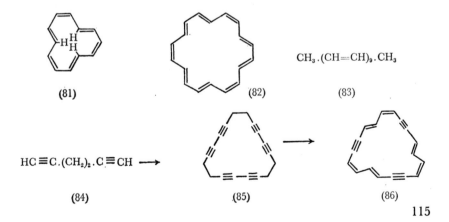

(81)

$CH_3 . (CH = CH)_9 . CH_3$

(82)

(83)

$HC \equiv C . (CH_2)_2 . C \equiv CH \longrightarrow$

(84)

(85)

(86)

115

light and air. Clearly it is much less stable than typical benzenoid compounds but it is nevertheless much more stable than the acyclic polyolefin (83) containing nine conjugated double bonds.

Catenanes. A possibility that has long excited the imagination of organic chemists is that sufficiently large rings with a big enough 'hole' in the middle might be able to form molecules comprising two or more rings interlocked in chain fashion.

An experiment which seems to indicate that such a compound can indeed be formed was carried out as follows. Diethyl tetratricontane-dioate (87, $R = Et$) was submitted to an acyloin condensation (p. 19) in the presence of the deuterium labelled large ring hydrocarbon (88). The hydrocarbon and acyloin fraction of the product were cleanly separated; however, it was found that the acyloin fractions contained a small but significant amount of deuterium. Furthermore, oxidation of the acyloin fraction to the dicarboxylic acid (87, $R = H$) liberated about 1% of the deuterated hydrocarbon (88). It appears, therefore, that this amount of hydrocarbon (88) had been firmly bound to the acyloin. The most likely explanation is that about 1% of the acyloin condensation occurred with the diester (87, $R = Et$) threaded through the large ring hydrocarbon to give an interlocked ring (89).

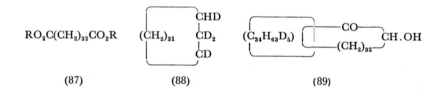

$$RO_2C(CH_2)_{32}CO_2R$$

(87)   (88)   (89)

Suggestions for Further Reading (Chapter 6)

1. 'The Importance of Many Membered Ring Compounds', V. PRELOG, in *Perspectives in Organic Chemistry*. Interscience Publ., Inc., New York, 1956, p. 96—early ideas on the conformation of medium rings, now in part replaced by reference 2.
2. J. D. DUNITZ and V. PRELOG, 'X-Ray Determined Conformation and Reactivity of Medium Rings', *Angewandte Chemie*, 1960, **72**, 896.
3. R. A. RAPHAEL, 'Recent Studies on Many Membered Rings', *Proc. Chem. Soc.*, 1962, p. 97—a highly concentrated survey of recent advances.
4. A. C. COPE, M. MARTIN and M. A. McKERVEY 'Transannular Reactions in Medium-sized Rings', *Quarterly Reviews*, 1966, **20**, 119.
5 R. A. RAPHAEL, 'Cyclo-octatetraene', in *Non-benzenoid Aromatic Compounds*, ed. D. Ginsburg, Interscience Publ. Inc., New York, 1959, p. 465.
6. J. SICHER, 'The Stereochemistry of Many-Membered Rings,' in *Progress in Stereochemistry*, Vol. 3, ed. P. B. D. de la Mare and W. Klyne, Butterworths, London, 1962.

INDEX

117

Robinson annelation 17

COPE TYPE REACTIONS 113
DEMJANOV TIFFENEAU 28
ANCHIMERIC ASSISTANCE 46.